The
JESUS
WE KNEW

✠

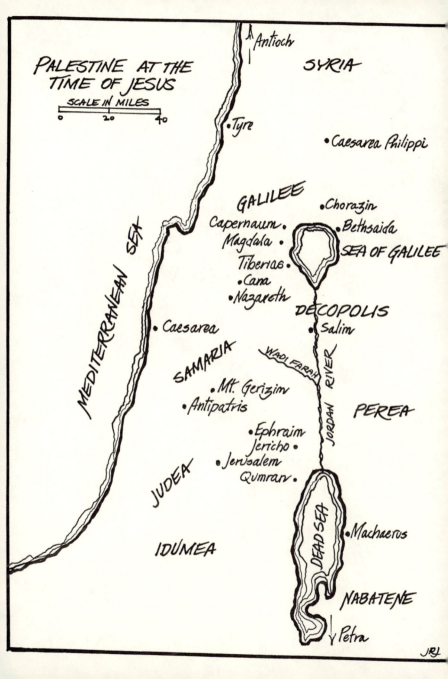

PALESTINE AT THE TIME OF JESUS

SCALE IN MILES
0   20   40

Antioch

SYRIA

Tyre

Caesarea Philippi

MEDITERRANEAN SEA

GALILEE

Chorazin
Capernaum
Bethsaida
Magdala
SEA OF GALILEE
Tiberias
Cana
Nazareth
DECOPOLIS
Caesarea
Salim

SAMARIA

WADI FARAH

JORDAN RIVER

Mt. Gerizim
Antipatris

PEREA

Ephraim
Jericho
Jerusalem
Qumran

JUDEA

DEAD SEA

Machaerus

IDUMEA

NABATENE

Petra

JRL

The
JESUS
WE KNEW

Remarkable Personal Stories
By Three Who Followed Him

JAMES R. JENNINGS

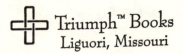

Triumph™ Books
Liguori, Missouri

Published by Triumph™ Books
Liguori, Missouri
An Imprint of Liguori Publications

Most scripture selections are taken from the New American Bible.
Copyright 1991, 1986, 1970 by the Confraternity of Christian Doctrine, Washington, D.C., and are used with permission.

Library of Congress Cataloging-in-Publication Data

Jennings, James R. (James Robert), 1923–
    The Jesus we knew : remarkable personal stories by three who
followed Him / James R. Jennings. — 1st ed.
        p. cm.
    Includes bibliographical references.
    ISBN 0-89243-555-0 : $15.95
    1. Bible stories, English—N.T. Mark.   I. Title
BS2585.5.J46   1993
232.9'5—dc20
                                                    93-19492
                                                         CIP

Printed in the United States of America

First Edition

In memory of
Isabel and Larry

Contents

Acknowledgments

In the early 1960s, I had the extraordinary good fortune to study Scripture under James Mara, S.J. at the Institute of Lay Theology, University of San Francisco. Mara's insightful treatment of the New Testament opened the eyes of this scriptural-illiterate cradle Catholic; otherwise, this book could not have been written.

More recently the persistent encouragement of my colleagues at the Campaign for Human Development, especially Mary Jo Shannon and Tom Ulrich, and the close attention to details by Victoria Cucciardo, were major contributions in writing this manuscript. William Holub should be added to the roster of the persistent ones who made this publication possible.

JAMES R. JENNINGS
March 18, 1993

Introduction

The three journeys portrayed here are stories of personal conversions; but they are more than that. These persons, Cornelius, James, and Joanna, personally experienced the cutting edge of Jesus' ministry. Their encounters with him, sometimes through others, caused them to see themselves differently, and therefore to be and act differently. That is, they experienced a personal change, traditionally called conversion.

In addition, their personal transformation caused them to see others, as well as their social environment, differently. Their conversion, therefore, was profoundly deeper and broader than personal; it radically transformed their worldview, and consequently the way they acted. Each of these sojourners, after their association with Jesus, faced profound choices.

Cornelius, the professional officer in the Roman army (Acts 10:1), was forced to reevaluate his career in the military. James (Mt 4:21), well positioned in his father's business, had to choose between a comfortable livelihood

in a fishing village in Galilee and a radically different lifestyle that might cost him his life. Joanna (Lk 8:3) perhaps faced the most serious choices of the three: loss of her marriage and her family or denial of her newly found self-identity and its consequences.

The writing of these three journeys of faith was prompted by several factors. First, many Catholics have a flawed image of Jesus' ministry. Second, Catholics want to know more about Jesus' life. The observation about the flawed image flows from personal experiences in conducting numerous workshops on social ministry with mainstream Catholics across the country, and the experience of others in religious education. The workshops are intended to expand Catholics' understanding of Jesus' ministry to include both the link between faith and the works of charity, as well as the link between faith and the pursuit of social justice.

One segment of the workshop includes an open discussion of the question: "What do you think Jesus did and said?" Consistently, the most frequent replies clustered around a litany of statements such as, "Jesus fed the hungry"; "He cured the sick"; "He worked miracles"; "He loved everyone." In the Midwest, a parishioner capsulized the sense of these litanies when he said, "I think Jesus set up the first social service agency in the Catholic Church two thousand years ago." Rarely did anyone suggest that Jesus confronted the authorities of his day.

In the second segment of the workshop, participants focus on the question: "Why do you think Jesus died?"

The replies have a marked consistency: "Jesus died for our sins"; "He opened the gates of heaven"; "It was his Father's will"; "He died so he could rise again"; "The authorities killed him." Occasionally, someone hesitantly offered: "The Jews killed him."

The workshop concludes with an open-ended discussion around the apparent paradox posed by the two sets of answers generated in the first two segments: If Jesus traveled throughout Palestine doing good work for people in need, why was he arrested and tried, convicted and executed by the ruling authorities of his day? The discussions explored such questions as how would various groups of people in Jesus' time react to his triumphant march into Jerusalem? The common people? The Jewish authorities? The Roman officials? If the Roman's prisoner, Barabbas, was a known insurgent (Lk 23:20), what was Pilate's motive for releasing him in exchange for Jesus? What did Jesus' apostles think was his mission, especially as revealed by their question, after his resurrection: "Lord, are you at this time going to restore the kingdom to Israel?" (Acts 1:6).

The ensuing discussions are lively and challenging. The participants were most comfortable in discussing their notions of what is formally called Christology (the term was used rarely), as they focused on the post-Easter events. They expressed it in terms of Christ the redeemer of humankind; the one who established his church and the sacraments. The general level of knowledge of Christ of faith seemed well grounded. Rarely did a note of unortho-

doxy surface, and it was quickly corrected by one of their peers. For the most part, participants disclose a profound difficulty placing Jesus and his actions within the social and political setting of his day. The Jesus of history, enmeshed in the political and economic conditions of the Roman colony of Palestine, seemed oblivious to them.

The primary focus of Jesus' ministry seems limited to his concern with personal conversion, calling individuals to a change of heart and to works of charity.[1] The common frame of reference seems to be that since Jesus dealt with spiritual matters and not with social issues, his ministry was nonpolitical and nonthreatening. His death resulted either from a mistaken notion by the authorities of Jesus' ministry, or it was part of the divine plan and therefore none of the principals at the time had any control over the events.

The editors of *U.S. Catholic* captured the essence of this widely-held image of Jesus, when they facetiously described him "as a nice person saying all those nice things, and here come old Pharisees and Jewish people who hated him and wanted to get rid of him." The popular perception is one in which Jesus "is a nice guy who taught love and mercy. And he just happened to be in the wrong place at the wrong time."[2]

A similar experience has been described by Michael Warren resulting from his work with retreats for Catholic teenagers. His concern is with the portrait of Jesus that is presented to middle-class young people. Warren maintains that the primary concern of middle-class people tends to

be a search for greater comfort and thus retreat masters tend to present a middle-class Jesus who comforts those who are moderately well-off and privileged. This emphasis "overlooks the Jesus who confronted and challenged, Jesus the upsetter." Warren calls for efforts to reclaim the Jesus who not only preached change of heart, but who called for change in structures as well. When the governing authorities realized this side of Jesus' preaching, Warren says, "They decided to get rid of him."[3]

When teenage students were asked what they believe is the core message of Christianity, William J. O'Malley reported their response "is a kind of ethical 'niceness' that would leave Christianity completely indistinguishable from the Boy Scouts or the Lions Club...You are Christians 'as long as you don't hurt anybody else.'" This perception is cultivated in homilies and hymns that portray Jesus, O'Malley asserts, "as almost exclusively that Good Shepherd who will pat our wooly heads and make everything nice and peaceful." The fault for this image of Jesus, as "the warm fuzzy," according to O'Malley, "rests with bishops, homilists, elementary and high school religious educators and parents."[4]

With O'Malley's inclusion of parents in his litany, we return full circle: Catholic adults, parents for the most, made up the majority of the participants of the social ministry workshops referred to initially in this introduction. The experience of educators and others seems to affirm the notion that the dominant image Catholics have of Jesus and his ministry is seriously incomplete.

Related to this phenomenon is the relationship of Catholics in general to the Bible. On the one hand the reading of the Bible has increased notably in the past ten years in virtually all groups of American Catholics. Other than attendance at Mass, Bible reading has become a major religious activity among young adult Catholics.[5] On the other hand, Catholics are biblical illiterates. Two out of three Catholics could not name the authors of the four Gospels. Six out of ten were unable to name Jesus as the person who delivered the Sermon on the Mount. On these findings Catholics scored poorest among other Christians by a large margin.

In summary, the first observation that prompted the writing of these stories — that Catholics have a flawed image of Jesus and his ministry — revolves around the following issues:

- Catholics want to learn more about social justice.

- They want to know more about the biblical roots of their faith.

- They have little awareness of how their faith relates to Jesus' ministry beyond providing direct services to individuals in need.

The second observation that motivated the writing of these stories flows from the first. The fact that Catholics were interested in deepening their knowledge of the Bible, and the relationship between their engagement in social ministry and in social change, provoked a search for

information about the social setting of the Gospels. The search disclosed the vastness of modern biblical scholarship about Jesus and his historical setting, as well as a body of literature written for other than scholars.[6]

A major aid in the search was Joachim Jeremias. In his extensive study of Jesus' parables, Jeremias cites the importance of Jesus' historical setting. He notes that the original context of all Jesus' sayings is their individual concrete situation. The challenge, then, is to situate Jesus' actions and intentions in that historical setting as far as possible.[7]

On this point, Pheme Perkins suggests that contemporary Christians need to shift their focus from those who believe Jesus' message to those who, as nonbelievers, heard it for the first time. Perkins' description of that original audience is enlightening: "Some may have been openly hostile. Perhaps some members of his audience saw themselves reflected or made fun of in the characters of the parables. Others may have been laughing to see a Pharisee or a rich person in a tight spot." The audiences included curious onlookers, the skeptical, religious authorities, those who were hoping to be persuaded, and finally, Jesus' own disciples. Each group might react quite differently to a story.[8]

Perkins also insists that the "sweet Jesus" caricature is dispelled when the social context of his public life is uncovered. The fate of Jesus was not because he said "nice things about lilies and swallows. No matter what else we say about Jesus, the brutal fact of who killed him and how it was done means that somehow we have to try to ex-

plain how he ended up in that situation."[9] While Jeremias pursues a search for the original social setting of Jesus' ministry, Perkins probes for a fresh imaginative approach to the original hearers of Jesus' words.

In the search for the characteristics of Jesus' time and place, Albert Nolan offers a challenging formula: read carefully between the lines of the four Gospels, and apply the information that is known about Jesus' contemporary situation.[10] This imaginative adventure, Nolan suggests, will disclose how Jesus' contemporaries lived and thought, and how they must have reacted to him. In this way we may come to a deeper understanding of what Jesus was doing and how those around were reacting to him.

General Comments about the Stories. The chronologies are fictionalized accounts that follow for the most part the general story line of Mark's Gospel.[11] The intention in each story is to stay within the general framework set by the Gospel accounts. The events that unfold are intended to be consistent within the limitations set by the Gospels and the political, religious, and cultural structures of Jesus' time. The fictional embellishments are introduced to provide body and texture to the story lines. But in all cases the intention is that they be consistent with the biblical record and other historical sources.

Liberties that are taken with the skeletal narratives of the Gospels are done so by the encouragement implied in the concluding verse of John's Gospel: "There are also many other things that Jesus did, but if these were to be de-

scribed individually, I do not think the whole world would contain the books that would be written" (Jn 21:25).

The reader is asked to imagine that these accounts are derived from several possible sources. One might have been a recovered ancient manuscript; another a lost letter or sections from a diary. The centurion's story might be thought of as a portion of his correspondence with a fellow officer in Rome. James' account might be excerpts from a lengthy letter to a Gentile convert. The episodes in Joanna's story, as the opening paragraph suggests, might have been written at the urging of one of the women leaders in the early church, perhaps Dorcas (Acts 9:39), or Lydia (Acts 16:11). Or perhaps it was Peter's wife (1 Cor 9:5). Since it is likely that Peter's wife knew that Mark's account of the Gospel was based heavily upon her husband's recollection of the days with Jesus, she may have asked Joanna to record her version of the Good News.

The intention of the stories is not to "explain" the mystery of Jesus. Faith in Jesus is deeper than any written words. The modest hope is that the stories may add some insights for those who believe that "God so loved the world that he gave his only Son, so that everyone who believes in him might not perish but might have eternal life" (Jn 3:16). Specifically, the stories intend to cast the events of Jesus' public life in such a light that his actions, which challenged the accepted political, social, and religious patterns of his day, will be more evident. And perhaps in this way Jesus' followers today will see more clearly the link between the practice of Christian faith and the pursuit of

social justice, and thus be more confident (even, perhaps, obligated) to pursue similar efforts on his behalf.

Each of the stories ends with an ellipsis, denoting that these accounts are only a fragment of the stories. Many more words would be needed to complete the testimonies of these three remarkable followers of Jesus.

The Good Centurion

Foreword

In addition to the data provided by the Gospel writers, "The Good Centurion" story relies heavily on other first-century writers as well as the work of present-day writers. The works of Flavius Josephus, written within several decades of Jesus' Ascension, provide many details about Pilate's conduct as governor during the Roman occupation of Palestine, the deployment of Roman troops, and the Jewish uprisings against the Romans during the occupation.[1] The details of the training and conduct of Roman soldiers, as well as their religious beliefs, draw on the work of moderns writers.[2] Jeremias' work was invaluable in providing important detailing to enhance the story's events.[3]

Cornelius' friend, Claudius Lysias, in the story (p. 13) located in Capernaum, is the name of the commander of the Jerusalem garrison who rescued Paul from a rioting crowd during his last visit in the city (Acts 21:30–32).

*The anti-Jewish tirades of the Roman army instructor,
Petronius, a fictional character (pp. 20, 23) are para-
phrases of Roman writers of that era.*[4]

*Other fictional characters are Simeon, a publican
(p. 15); Justin, a senior centurion (p. 17); Lucius, commander of the Antonio (p. 26); Jonathan, a chief priest (p. 26);
and Abram, a rabbi (p. 30).*

*What follows is Cornelius' recollections of events lead-
ing up to his crucial career decision.*

In your last letter you asked if I ever met Jesus. Regrettably, I can't say I met him or had a conversation with him.
The most I can say is, I saw him once and heard him talking. It was a brief episode under very trying circumstances;
it was clear he was in trouble at the time.

As I remember it, Jesus didn't stand out in the crowd.
I had to ask someone to point him out to me. When
I got close enough to hear him, I could see him more
clearly. There was something unusual about him; I've often
thought about it. But more about that later.

I said Jesus was in trouble. That's an understatement.
So was I, for that matter. For me, the whole affair began
a month before. I was stationed here at military headquarters in Caesarea with my unit, but I expected to be assigned
temporary duty in Jerusalem. During the years I was stationed at Caesarea, I drew the special annual festival duty
in Jerusalem. Jews flood into the city for the Passover from

as far away as Rome and Alexandria. The population of Jerusalem rises during the festival to over one hundred thousand people from its normal size of about twenty-five thousand. Our standard military procedure is to reinforce the permanent infantry unit stationed there during the Passover. To forestall any outbreak of violence, reinforcements from the garrisons at Capernaum and Joppa as well as Caesarea are sent to Jerusalem.

I said I was anticipating the temporary assignment in Jerusalem; the fact is, I was looking forward to it. Not that the city was particularly attractive; but army life can be boring. Our mission is to keep the peace in the provinces at all cost. When our military presence achieves its objective, peace prevails. As a consequence, our troops, trained for combat, become restless when they are inactive. As one of our veteran centurions put it: "Many of our recruits have never struck a blow in anger other than in a tavern." The challenge for us officers was to find something for the men to do, otherwise an unoccupied army may soon become demoralized or even dangerous. The annual assignment to Jerusalem broke the monotony.

It also gave me a chance to see my old friend, Claudius Lysias, a centurion stationed at the Capernaum garrison, who also regularly drew the Jerusalem assignment. We first met years before when we were young army recruits. What impressed me about Claudius, from the very first, was his certainty. He always seemed to know what he had to do. Roman law for him was like a light that helped him see what had to be seen. He was fair and honest, and always

operated with a keen sense of his rank and authority, but always within the law.

Of course, if I had the choice between going to Jerusalem or to Antioch, it's Antioch, every time! Given the choice, every centurion wanted to be assigned there. As you know, it's the jewel of the East. But Antioch was not to be. In any case, as I said, I was looking forward to the posting notice. Finally, one day, it came:

> Centurion Cornelius, commander of Infantry Unit Three, of the Italica Cohort, is ordered to prepare his men for deployment in Jerusalem in the company of the Governor.
>
> Departure: Dawn, April 2.
>
> /Signed/ Pontius Pilate,
>   Governor of Samaria and Judea

✠

After the first day's march out of Caesarea, we made camp on the outskirts of Antipatris. The men quickly turned the area into a Roman encampment: Large tents for the men were raised at four corners to form a large open square; the commissary was unpacked and set up for the meals. The field equipment was deployed; camp chairs, work tables and bunks were set in place. In the center of the square Pilate's tent was erected. It was very much larger than the others; big enough to accommodate the governor, his trappings, and a number of slaves. The tent was

outfitted with large ribbons, and silk curtains hung at the entrance where a large canopy covered the doorway. Sentries were posted. And finally, with due ceremonial pomp, the eagle-standard of the Italica Legion was hoisted next to the governor's tent on a fifteen-foot standard. The whole operation, to the pride of our unit, was completed literally in a matter of minutes.

Shortly before sunset, the local Roman appointee, a publican named Simeon and two elders came to the camp-site and asked to see the governor. This was a formal ceremony; it was repeated every time Pilate made a trip to Jerusalem, and at every town in which we camped. Pilate came out of his tent, sat on an elaborately decorated camp chair with two fully bedecked soldiers with lance and shield on either side of him. The guards were selected for this duty from among the largest men in the unit; they towered over the visitors. Finally after Pilate was comfortably seated, one of the guards motioned to the publican to step forward.

Standing before Pilate, the publican slowly read from a prepared text, welcoming the Roman Legion to the town. The town's men had brought gifts for Pilate, which they handed to the guards: lavish linens and brocaded silks from India. During the entire affair, Pilate never spoke or stood up or in any way gave an expression of acknowledgment or pleasure. At the end, he got up and returned to his tent; the visitors bowed, turned and left the camp.

That evening, after dinner, I couldn't get the episode out of my mind. Especially the elders. They seemed so pitiful.

They never said a word. They hung back several paces behind the publican with a timid expression on their faces. They acted like beggars.

Not that Pilate seemed intentionally rude to them. He was playing a role, as were they. He was the symbol of Rome, powerful and imperturbable. They were the obedient servants of their superiors. Who was the more pitiful, I wondered, the elders or Pilate? Both of them were caught in some mysterious plot, destined to play out their respective roles, like a Greek play I had seen in Antioch. All the players are caught by fate; they have no choices and in the end they are doomed.

The irony was that the elders knew, as did most of the men in the camp, that Pilate was a scoundrel. How much they knew, of course, I couldn't be certain. What was certain, however, was that I knew it. In the five years that Pilate was governor, his conduct was outrageous. For example, I knew that wrapped in the cloth gifts he received were packets containing thousands of denarii, ten times a centurion's annual pay. I knew of other bribes he had taken. I also knew of senseless floggings and executions he had ordered.

In this tragic scene I knew all the players were not caught in the same way. The elders had little choice. They knew that their town, their livelihood, their families, their very existence was almost totally dependent upon the actions of others; specifically the power of our occupying army and the caprices of the governor, Pilate.

Pilate, on the other hand, clearly had choices. He had

power — the enormous resources of the emperor. At Pilate's command the elders and publicans literally lived or died. So Pilate had choices: to exercise his power arrogantly or benignly, with malevolence or benevolence.

But I had seen Pilate for too long and too close up to think he could use his power in a just way. I realized Pilate had been wounded. Not like the elders; they had capitulated to Pilate's power and in exchange for their self-respect they gained survival. Pilate had capitulated to the addictive force of power itself. He didn't seem to be able to help himself. Each of them, in his own way, seemed trapped.

And what about me, I thought? Am I trapped? Have I no options? I knew Pilate was disreputable, but there was nothing I could do. As a Roman army officer, I had sworn to be loyal to the emperor and obedient to his appointed leaders. I had taken an oath that I would do nothing to dishonor his empire. I could not help but wonder if I was to be merely a curious observer — a kind of innocent bystander, passing my silent judgment on these trapped victims?

I slept fitfully that first night out. As I slipped in and out of sleep, I recalled an incident that happened a short time before my tour of duty at Caesarea. One of the senior centurions, Justin, told me about a confrontation between Pilate and some of the Jews from Jerusalem.

Pilate had been governor at Caesarea for about a year

when he gave a secret order to have standards with portraits of Caesar Tiberius mounted on them and placed outside the Temple in Jerusalem. He sent a unit of his palace guards undercover to Jerusalem carrying the standards. After they arrived in the city, they waited until well into the night and then positioned the standards at one of the Temple gates. At dawn when the townspeople saw what had happened, they were furious. By noon, the city was in an uproar. "As any recruit knows," Justin said, "the Jews are absolutely opposed to having an image or an engraving, even a statue, set out in their city. It violates one of their most sacred rules."

Finally, the elders calmed the crowd, and organized a people's march to Caesarea where they demanded that Pilate remove the images. They marched to command headquarters, and sent a delegation to appeal to Pilate. He refused to talk to them, but he gave instructions for the crowd to assemble in the stadium in a week and he would give them an answer at that time.

"That day at the stadium," Justin recalled, "was one of the worst days of my fifteen years in the army." Pilate ordered all the infantry units to dress in full armor and to take up positions outside the stadium. After the crowd entered, he planned for the troops to march in and surround the protesters. When he mounted the podium he would tell them that if they did not accept the images of Caesar, he would command the troops to kill them all on the spot.

"Were any of the Jews armed?" I asked. "No, I don't think any of them even had a shield, much less a sword.

That's what bothered me from the time I'd received the orders that morning: anticipating what I'd do if Pilate gave the signal."

"What did you do?"

"It was not so much what I did. It's what the Jews did." Pilate gave his speech; he told them to accept the images, leave the stadium and return peacefully to Jerusalem. Not one of them moved. Finally, Pilate raised his hands, we drew our swords, and the entire crowd, as if they had rehearsed it, fell to the ground in unison and began chanting: "We would rather die than transgress the Law."

Justin was standing about thirty feet from the podium when the senior centurion of Pilate's palace guard rushed over to Pilate. They talked for several minutes. Finally, Pilate walked off the podium muttering, "These people are fools."

The centurion then mounted the podium and announced, "Pilate commands you to return to Jerusalem. The standards will be removed. It is Caesar's will!" With that the crowd dispersed and returned to Jerusalem.

I asked him why Pilate tried to impose the standards? Was he following orders from Rome? Justin said, "No. It was the use of raw power." I don't think Pilate ever forgave the Jews for that embarrassment he suffered. There can only be one reason he tried to push Caesar's standard on the Jewish people, the sheer exercise of power; the arrogance of power.

✠

Our second day was a repeat of the first day. After the day's march, we encamped on the south side of Jericho and Pilate was visited by the local publican, Zacchaeus and two of the city's elders. Again, as in Antipatris, there were the public gifts, the secret bribes, and the humiliation of the Jews.

That evening I couldn't get Zacchaeus out of my mind. I kept recalling how he groveled before Pilate. I wondered what it would take for Zacchaeus and other Jews to rise up and rebel against us. Of course, we had the troops, they had the humiliations; we had the armor, all they had were promises.

As Roman army officers we were schooled in the local Jewish culture and history. I remember well my training as an eager young centurion, fresh from Rome, when I was first assigned in Antioch to the Fifth Army under the Roman Legate, Quirinius. A senior centurion, Petronius, a twenty-year veteran of Roman campaigns in the colonies around the Mediterranean Sea, lectured us on the events of the previous fifty years or so.

We learned that Julius Caesar had installed Herod the Great as his puppet king of the Roman colony. Herod had first attracted Caesar's attention when he put down an uprising in Galilee many years before. All went reasonably well in the region until Herod's death, which was followed by a series of uprisings.

One of Herod's sons, Archelaus, had assumed his father's place, but he was no match for the situation. With the Passover festival approaching and Jerusalem begin-

ning to be filled with pilgrims, mobs demanded revenge for some of Herod's outrageous actions. Archelaus panicked and sent a small unit of his troops to attack the crowds. The soldiers were vastly outnumbered and were wiped out. Archelaus then ordered his full military force deployed against the crowd and more than three thousand Jews were killed. The Passover festival was in shambles, and the event enkindled bitter resentment of the people against the Roman occupation.

A second incident occurred when a senior centurion, Sabinus, tried to commandeer the funds in the Temple treasury before Herod's heirs could claim it. He led an army unit into Jerusalem and when people in the city discovered Sabinus' move, they attacked his troops. The attack was so fierce and sustained that Varus, the legate of Syria, was forced to lead a company of reinforcements to subdue the uprising. When the fighting ended, Varus ordered the crucifixion of two thousand insurgents and the imprisonment of hundreds of others.

About this same time, trouble broke out in Galilee under the leadership of a rebel named Judas, son of Ezechias. After Judas and his men raided the arsenal at the Capernaum garrison, they set off on an armed rebellion that could only be quelled weeks later by the deployment of Capernaum's full military force.

Further south, a pretender to the throne, Simon of Perea, collected a band of followers and some weapons, and attacked Jericho. They burned the royal palace Herod had built and a number of stately mansions in the city.

An infantry unit from Jerusalem successfully put down the rebels.

Another uprising broke out under a shepherd who paraded about the region wearing a crown on his head. He led his men on raiding expeditions in the region, killing Roman soldiers and Jews accused of being collaborators. The uprising required the best of our soldiers to capture and neutralize the rebels.

I remember at this point in his extended presentation, Petronius seemed to warm up to the subject. He insisted that all of this was merely a prologue. "The best — or the worst, from our point of view," he said, "is yet to come. How many of you have heard of the Zealots?" Of course, we'd all had contact with them. Their tactics covered the field: disruption, terrorism, intimidation. Any persons they suspected of collaborating with the Roman authorities might be picked off, their property looted, their livestock run off and their homes burned.

"This Zealot business all started about twenty-five years ago," Petronius said, "when Coponius was sent to Caesarea to be governor of the province." When Caesar Augustus became convinced that Archelaus was no match for the rebellious nature of the Jews, he removed him. Coponius served under the direct authority of Quirinius, legate of Syria. Trouble started when he ordered a census and a reassessment of Jewish property to determine the amount of the tax for the empire.

Joazor, the high priest, joined Coponius in the public announcement in an attempt to lend legitimacy to the

order, but that seemed to inflame the radicals. Two Jewish leaders from Galilee, Judas and Sadduc, a Pharisee, refused to comply with the command. They attracted a small band of followers who responded to their fanatical call to nationalism, under the guise of religious fervor. To pay taxes to Rome, they maintained, would violate their religious belief. Only their god deserved such allegiance. "God alone is our leader and master," became their rallying cry.

Petronius seemed to delight in giving details of the Roman attack against the rebels in which both Judas and Sadduc were killed along with most of their followers; Petronius led the attack.

He always laced these lectures with anti-Jewish quips: "The Jews harbor deep hatred of all Romans...of all the enslaved people, Jews are the most contemptible....They are loathsome, superstitious atheists....They were expelled from Egypt because they were lepers....Their custom of resting on the Sabbath originated because they incurred a pelvic ailment when they left Egypt, that has forced them to rest every seven days....It is said that every seven years they capture a stranger, take him into their Temple, and cut him into small pieces...."

"But obviously," he said, "Judas' death didn't end it. We know that some of their followers have continued to resist the authority of Caesar and undermine Rome's presence in the region. They continue to this day to lead a resistance movement."

That's because the Jews, Petronius said, have a dangerous strain of sedition in their history. They labor under a

sort of lost kingdom mystique. They remember that they once were an independent people with their own monarchy that ruled a vast region that was rich and powerful. But unlike the Greeks and Egyptians who also once were independent monarchies and have since submitted to the movement of history, these people refused to forget their past.

Petronius told us that remembering for Jews is part of their religious ritual. Their religious beliefs foster the notion that their kingdom will rise again under some anointed savior-king who will liberate them. The people's memory runs deep — at a depth of some five hundred years. They are possessed by a kind of messiah complex. They expect a popular leader will rise up like their King David with support from their god and lead the people to political freedom.

So when Pilate took up his post in Caesarea, Petronius said, he found that he was the governor of a colony that had been racked by continuous violence for several decades. For Petronius, the Roman army's presence in Judea was clear: "Our job is to resist the Jew's 'kingdom' aspirations at all cost."

That night, I thought about Zacchaeus. Little Zacchaeus with his humiliation and promises, what chance did he have against Roman military power?

✤

On the third day of the march, as we approached Jerusalem, Pilate was in his glory. When we broke camp in

Jericho, he ordered the troops into full battle gear; not because he expected any trouble. Quite the contrary, he wanted to display Roman military force. On the first two days of the march, the men wore lightweight, noncombat uniforms. Battle attire meant leather trousers with metal reinforcements, hobnailed sandals, bronze helmets, large oblong shields and swords. During the march from Jericho, the soldiers formed in columns on both sides of the road with Pilate, in full ceremonial dress, mounted on a large white Arabian stallion following behind the standard bearers.

When we were within several miles of the city gate cheering crowds came out to greet us. Advanced scouts had been sent into the city the night before to alert the Temple authorities about Pilate's arrival the next day. We were not surprised therefore to see the crowds; the surprise would have been if the people hadn't been there. It was in the interest of the high priest, Caiaphas, to appease Pilate, as it was in Pilate's interest that the high priest maintain a subservient population. Neither's interest was served by being antagonists. In a very real sense, the two men were locked together; not in an affectionate embrace. Rather, neither dared to let the other go for fear of attack. Our Caesarean units entered the city in late afternoon and marched directly to the Antonia, the Roman garrison, where we were to be billeted. The units from the garrisons at Capernaum and Joppa had arrived about midday.

We arrived about two weeks before the celebration of

the Passover, but we immediately got down to business. I was ordered to accompany Lucius, commander of the Antonia, to meet with Jonathan, one of the Temple's chief priests to discuss the deployment of our troops. Among Jonathan's duties was that of Temple chief of police. Each year the deployment of Roman troops was a sensitive matter with the Temple authorities. During these feasts we always stationed armed troops on the balconies around the interior wall of the Temple area to forestall any rioting that might break out.

I had had similar meetings with him on previous occasions, and the substance of this meeting was no exception. It was short, formal, and routine. "Please, understand," Lucius said, "our troops have no intention of interfering in your religious ceremonies. Our only purpose here is to maintain order, and our troops fully understand that. You have your job; we have ours. If we work together I am sure all will go well."

"I understand," Jonathan said.

We shook hands and parted. I didn't see him again until a week later at the ceremony of the high priest's vestments. This event had also become routine, but in its own way it had great significance. For years we kept the ceremonial vestments of the Jewish high priest in the Antonia, and only on special occasions, such as Passover, did we release them to the incumbent high priest. Since he was viewed as the highest ranking authority among the Jews, the tactic was intended to symbolize the power of Rome, and thereby be a safeguard against local rebellion. So long

as order was maintained among the Jews, the robes were released to the high priest on the first day of their Holy Week.

I was again ordered to join Lucius. As we marched down the stairs that joined the Antonia garrison and the Temple's Court of the Gentiles, we were flanked by a squad of fully armored Roman guards. By this time there was a crowd in the Court; we encouraged the Jewish leaders to have large numbers of people turn out to view the ceremony. Lucius presented the vestments to Caiaphas.

"May the peace continue," Lucius said.

As Caiaphas accepted the robes, he replied, "Shalom." With Jonathan at his side, they retreated into the Court of the Israelites and we returned to the Antonia.

I immediately began to look for Claudius, because I knew his unit had arrived from Capernaum sometime before mine. And I had so much I wanted to talk with him about. It was almost six months since we'd been together, and each time we met we spent long evenings in deep conversation. Recently we were able to get together about three or four times a year because of his special assignments at headquarters in Caesarea.

When I finally located him, we began talking as we always did, picking up right where we left off at the last meeting. Well into the night, I broached the subject that had been pressing on me: my disappointment, I finally called it disgust, with Pilate. The use of force, I could accept. As a career military man, I was well trained in its use. "Force, to keep the peace," I said. "But not to intimidate

or humiliate defenseless people and certainly not to extract outlandish bribes."

What's worse, I said, is that Pilate's conduct caused me to question some of the basic beliefs I had about serving "the sacred triad:" the emperor, the empire and the gods.

"Slow down," Claudius said. "You haven't had it so bad. The army has been good to you."

He was right. Everything I did in the early years of my military service, I saw as service to Caesar, Rome, and the gods. If I had been asked to say which of the three was the most important, I couldn't have answered. All three had been blended into one common image for me.

Over the years I have frequently thought about all of this, and the longer I served in the army, the more I become aware that my military service was not for the triad. It was principally for me. I served in the army for my own personal gain. As a young man the army was good for me. It gave me a good experience of discipline that I needed. It deepened my sense of values, like duty and honor. I'm not sure that I would have developed them if it hadn't been for the army. They were drummed into us as career military officers.

In my early years in the army the notion of absolute loyalty to the emperor and ultimately to the commands of my superiors was supreme. The idea that "The commander's order is law" must be pervasive for soldiers. We were drilled in the concept that military campaigns are life and death, victory or defeat; there is not room for doubt or debate.

I served with men from Athens and Corinth, Antioch and Alexandria. Some were good soldiers and loyal Roman citizens. I served with some who were courageous and some who were not. I was strengthened by their signs of courage and humbled by their lapses into human weakness. It was not always clear to me what I was learning or where it was leading me. What was becoming more apparent in recent years, though, was my personal gains from these experiences were not sufficient for me. To maintain order in the empire, to give obedience to the emperor, and to worship the gods were not enough. The worst days were those in which I questioned the value of maintaining order in the empire.

"Hold on," Claudius said, breaking into my tirade. "You have a short memory, my friend. Have you forgotten what we have done? We have brought law and order to an undisciplined world." Claudius went on with his litany: paved roads where there had been mud sloughs; water flowing through Roman-built aqueducts into lands that had been parched for centuries; everywhere people are now safe from fear of brigands and pirates. "Have you forgotten?" Claudius said, "Rome has the mission to imprint its law and culture on the world. That's Pax Romana! And you and I are part of that mission."

"There, you have said it: Pax Romana. Who gave us Romans this mission?" I asked. "The law and order you're talking about is peace on our terms, Roman terms. We have thousands of troops deployed at strategic points around the Mediterranean. That's Pax Romana. You don't

think for one minute that if Pilate announced to these people that our army is going to leave Judea in the morning,
that they'd beg us to stay? For us, peace is the order that
follows the unconditional surrender of those we defeat.
But is that kind of order enough?"

"What would I do," I asked Claudius, "if Pilate gave
me a command to commit one of his outrageous cruel-
ties like that dreadful execution episode last year? Obey
the order out of respect for the office he holds, despite
the fact that I have total disrespect for the man?" Claudius replied to my rhetorical question with an answer that
matched the rhetoric of mine, "You'd do what you have to
do."

It was that night that I first confided to him about my
interest in Judaism. About a year before a friend in Caesarea had introduced me to a rabbi, Abram, who agreed
to explore the writings of their prophets with me. "I'm not
surprised," Claudius said. "But I am curious. Why did you
do it?"

I told him that for some time the triad had begun to lose
its hold for me. The first thing that began to slide in recent
years was the gods. Every city or town that I'd ever been
sent to, has a god. There are gods of the home, of rivers
and trees, gods who decide our fate. Everybody can create
their own gods; the only limit is a person's imagination.
Each of us carries a god around with us. The coins in our
purse bear the inscription: "Augustus was a god and our
great Tiberius Caesar is his son."

But I knew that the real god worshiped in the army is

the Roman eagle, a big golden eagle with its talons filled with silver-gilded lightning bolts. We stand it up in its own special chapel where we worship it and swear our loyalty to it. That's not enough for me, I told Claudius. "That's not enough to hold on to or to believe in. I feel like I am adrift, disconnected from reality. I am desperately frightened."

Claudius said, "Old friend, you are taking all of this too seriously. I put my trust in fate. Fate is blind, inconsistent, elusive, capricious. I know I do not control events. We are all so much at the mercy of fate that fate is our god."

"I can't accept that," I replied. I related to him that a centurion friend told me he wanted the headstone on his grave to read: "I was; I am not; I do not care."

"Well, I do care," I told Claudius. "I care about what's happening to me now and what's going to happen later."

Claudius, a real friend, didn't say anything for a while. Finally, he said, "Be careful."

✠

The next week we settled into a routine. In the morning briefing there were the typical reports of occasional street fights in the city, robberies on the roads leading into Jerusalem, several murders and rumors of uprisings. With more than one hundred thousand people crowding into the tiny walled city, we expected some disturbances.

It was during one of the midweek briefings, that Lucius read the following report:

Last night, the Fourth Unit of the Jerusalem garrison arrested a person known as Barabbas, which may be an alias.

It is not clear what the exact crime was that he committed. One report is that Barabbas and two others, identities unknown, attacked three soldiers of the Fourth Unit, killing two and wounding a third. The prisoners are being held in the Antonia awaiting execution.

One of the centurions, a recruit from Joppa, spoke up, "That's an odd name, Barabbas. Doesn't it mean, Son of the Father?"

"Yes, it is odd," Lucius said. "One of the Temple guards who was on the scene at the time of the arrest, said that an informer told him he'd learned that Barabbas is one of the sons of Judas the Galilean. And to hide his identity he doesn't use the name Jesus Barjudas. He chooses the alias, 'Son of the Father,' 'Bar Abbas.'"

Lucius went on to report that his special agents who had infiltrated the Zealots some months ago, believe they had uncovered a plot to lead an insurrection against the Temple authorities and possibly our garrison as well. Lucius added that one of the ringleaders was thought to be Barabbas. He seemed to be confident that a full-scale uprising was unlikely, because of the arrests his men had made. However, he wanted us to be extra cautious. He reminded us: "There is only one reason your men are in Jerusalem. Keep the peace at any cost."

None of us needed to be reminded of the reason we had been deployed. The city was alive with rumors of uprisings and insurrection. I reported the events to my men. They all knew the name, Judas the Galilean. It was not possible to be stationed in the Judean province and not know the exploits of his followers.

Since our unit's assignment was restricted to the Temple area, the prospect of us being involved in an uprising seemed quite unlikely. If a major insurrection was to break out it would probably begin outside the walls of the city and would therefore be the concern of the Roman regulars assigned to Antonia who patrolled the entire surrounding area, and the Jewish Temple police who had the whole city and its environs under their close surveillance.

About a week later, Lucius had one of his special agents brought into the briefing room. "We have reason to believe," the agent said, "that a person from Galilee, a man called Jesus, has come to Jerusalem under the pretense of celebrating the Holy Jewish feast and that he and his followers may invade the city at any time." According to the informer's agents, the Galileans had gathered about four miles east of Jerusalem in the town of Bethany, in the home of one of their allies. He also reported that they planned to join the caravan of pilgrims from the Galilean region and march into Jerusalem in a day or two. "Be on the alert!" was Lucius' remark that ended the briefing.

Claudius was on morning patrol duty that day and did

not learn of the report until later when I filled him in on the details of the briefing.

"I don't understand," he said, "what Lucius is concerned about."

"What do you mean?" I asked.

"Well, if the leader he is talking about is the same Jesus I met in Capernaum, we don't have anything to worry about. He's harmless."

Claudius proceeded to relate the experiences he had had with Jesus. He had heard stories of incredible things Jesus was doing in the Galilean region. So, on an outside chance that Jesus could help one of Claudius' slaves who was dying of a paralysis, he had the town elders seek out Jesus. "Just like that," Claudius said, "Jesus cured him. I must say, though, I was hesitant about contacting him. I wasn't certain," Claudius continued, "how the town elders would interpret my actions, since I was not sure how well Jesus was accepted by them."

I knew that Claudius had had difficulties in Capernaum. Our garrison there was right in the center of Galilee, historically a hotbed of sedition, dating back to the days of Judas the Zealot. Claudius had worked at ingratiating the local Jewish leadership, in an attempt to defuse any hostility toward the Roman presence. His efforts included detailing a unit of the garrison's construction corps to rehabilitate the town's synagogue.

Claudius told me about the times that he had met with Jesus for extended discussions. His interest was initially sparked by Jesus' growing public following. With

increasing frequency Jesus' name appeared on reports from Claudius' deputies about Jesus' activities. Claudius also had reports within Herod's court, from Manaen, a close friend of Herod and from Chuza, Herod's steward, that Herod was gravely suspicious of Jesus.

Claudius arranged through several Jewish elders of the town to meet Jesus at night in a secret place. Recalling his military training, Claudius asked, "What is it, Jesus, that you are trying to do? Are you some kind of messiah?"

Jesus went on to tell him that the kingdom of his God was about to come to pass and he was compelled to go about the countryside and alert everyone.

"Are you saying that in order for your kingdom to come, you plan to attack my troops and drive the Roman army out of Palestine?"

"No, no," Jesus said, "nothing like that." He went on to say that he was not a Zealot and was not connected with their movement. His purpose was not to repeat the conventional way of one armed group revolting against another. As he said, the Romans did that against the Greeks, and the Greeks before them, attacking the Syrians and so on and so on. His purpose called for a new revolution.

"If not with swords and chariots," Claudius asked, "then how?"

The two of them met frequently over a period of several months and Claudius said there was a resoluteness about Jesus that impressed him and even frightened him, although he was hesitant to admit it. But the discussions

always came down to the same question: How did Jesus expect his kingdom to come about?

Jesus always said his way does not call for a repeat of the old, wornout methods. Rather it calls for something very different. On one occasion he said, "You do not think that I, a Jew, would enter your house, since you are a Gentile. You and I are very different, perhaps, even enemies. But, I say I would welcome an invitation to your home."

"Why," Claudius asked, "would you do that?"

"Invite me and see," Jesus said. "While we are different in many ways, I do not hate you; I love you. When I look at you, I see a brother. You are created by the same God who created every person who is alive or who ever lived. We are all brothers and sisters of the same Father, who is God of all there is."

During one of these meetings Claudius said, he told Jesus that he did not understand much of what he said and what he thought he understood was so unbelievable as to be ridiculous. "But if I understand what you are saying," Claudius said, "you are not a direct violent threat to my way of life. You are more dangerous than that. If you were violent, you might try to kill me and that would be the end of it for me in a flash, or for you, if I countered your attack. But what you want is for me to change my whole way of living and believing and acting. You want me to change and if I did, I might never get over it. And that could really be painful for the rest of my life."

Jesus said, "You are perhaps closer to the truth than you know."

Claudius said his conversations with Jesus were always the same: fascinating and incredible.

An episode occurred two days later that brings me back to the encounter with Jesus that I mentioned in the beginning of this narrative. I was on duty as the officer of the day. The sergeant in charge of the men patrolling the balcony on the east side of the Temple's enclosure reported to me that one of the Jews was arguing with the authorized agents who had set up their booths to house moneychangers and sellers of sacrificial animals and birds. These activities were approved by the Temple authorities and provided necessary services for the pilgrims who thronged into the Temple to participate in the worship. The sergeant said the disturbance seemed to be getting out of hand.

I told him to summon someone in authority in the Temple. When Jonathan arrived, I asked him if he knew what the disturbance was about.

"The Levites tell me," Jonathan said, "that a Galilean named Jesus is having a little squabble with some of the merchants. I don't think it is anything you need to be concerned about. It will all settle down shortly."

Neither of us believed that. We both had information, from different sources, that the Galilean might not be as harmless as a mere squabbler. In the morning briefing, we had received information that two of his associates, on the previous day, had stolen a colt in a nearby town. Bethany,

I think it was. When they were stopped, one of them said: "It's all right. The Lord needs it. We will return it when he is finished with it."

The Galilean then proceeded to ride toward Jerusalem mounted on the colt, with crowds of people cheering and shouting along the way: "Save us, we pray!" "Blessed is he who comes in the name of the Lord, the king of the Israel!" "Blessed is he who comes as king!" Some of the people in the crowd spread their cloaks on the roadway as the parade moved on toward the city. Others spread branches they had cut from the trees. A Temple guard asked one of the people in the crowd, "Who is this man?"

The guard said, "This is the Jesus from Galilee." The officer then worked his way through the crowd and up to the Galilean and told him to silence the crowd.

"If you try to stop them," Jesus said, "the stones of the Temple will cry out."

One of Lucius' informants reported that when the mob reached the crest of the hill that overlooks Jerusalem, the Galilean halted the colt, looked out over the city and evidently began to sob. One of his allies went up to him and asked, "What is the trouble, Rabbi?"

Jesus answered, "These people do not understand what it is that makes for peace."

The informer reported that he said, "Unless they change their ways, their enemies will surround this city with fortifications, and they and their children will be crushed to the ground."

"What are we to do?" one of them asked.

The crowd swarmed in upon Jesus, and the informant could not hear Jesus' reply.

Lucius went on to report that the mob then continued on to the city and into the Temple area. The Galilean and a group of his followers who clustered around him walked through the Court of the Gentiles. They left the Temple area about dusk, and headed east toward Bethany. By then the mob had dispersed.

As Jonathan and I hurried with two soldiers toward the east side of the enclosure, his assurance that the squabble would be short-lived seemed overly optimistic. Down below from the area of the merchants' quarters, where the money-exchange and selling stalls were set up, I could hear people shouting, but I couldn't make out what they were saying. When we arrived at a stairway, I told Jonathan to lead the way; I stayed back until he had gotten to the bottom of the steps. I signaled to him to move on toward the crowd; I didn't want either my men or me to be seen by the crowd on the chance that our presence might spark an even greater outburst.

When the clamor finally receded, I knew I had to see for myself what was going on. When I got to the foot of the stairs I saw people milling about; some of the merchants were trying to retrieve doves that were flying about the colonnades. Some of them were propping up their tables and stalls. Others were scurrying on the floor, gathering up coins that had been scattered about the courtyard. My attention was focused on finding the person who appar-

ently led yesterday's march into the city and who started this commotion.

But I couldn't see anyone who stood out. As I said earlier I asked one of Jonathan's Temple guards to point him out to me. He pointed toward a group of men gathered around a trader's stall and finally, for the first time I was close enough to see and hear this notorious Galilean. Everyone around Jesus could see that he was in trouble; and surely he must have known it, too. What was striking, considering the circumstances, was the expression on his face. It was a smile; not a mask. Rather it was as a warm light from inside. He seemed to be enjoying the whole affair. It's just that his expression, his whole manner — the way he looked and moved — seemed to say that everything was all right. More than that, he seemed to be saying that what he was doing was good. In any case he seemed to be enjoying it.

The merchants around Jesus were clearly angry, but he stood in their midst, calmly, speaking softly. So softly, that at first I could only hear an occasional hostile merchant:

"What are you trying to do?" Or another, "I have a license from the high priest to operate here. What right do you have to do this?"

Through the din of the crowd Jesus continued to speak softly and slowly, although I still could not hear him. Finally, I got close enough that his quiet voice penetrated the clamor. But it wasn't only his voice; again, it was his entire manner. He seemed to be at ease with himself; so right about what he was doing.

I heard him say to an old merchant, "Where there is a sad heart the spirit is broken. But a glad heart wears a happy face." "Come on," he said, "let me see you smile."

The old man looked at his empty dove cages and asked, "What do I have to smile about?"

Jesus said, "Unless there is more for you than caged doves, you will never smile."

Whenever I relate this episode to anyone who has ever seen Jesus, they always said they remember him the same way: joy-filled, with a kind of radiance, happiness. However, given the circumstances, he seemed to say, "It's all right, enjoy the moment." I remember telling Claudius about the episode and he began to laugh.

"I know exactly what you're talking about. I experienced it when I was with him those evenings in Capernaum."

A few days later, Lucius opened the morning briefing by bringing Jonathan into the session and having him give an account of the previous night's episode. "Last night," Jonathan stated, "a unit of the Temple police, accompanied by a squad of troops from Antonia, broke up a meeting of an armed band of Galileans just outside of the city. After a brief skirmish, the leader of the group, a rabbi, was arrested."

Jonathan went on to say that the prisoner was brought before Caiaphas and the Sanhedrin, where, under interrogation, he claimed to be the messiah. He also reported

that there were several witnesses who testified that Jesus threatened to attack the Temple. Caiaphas, Jonathan said, intends to bring the prisoner before Pilate.

At that point, Lucius dismissed Jonathan and then proceeded to detail for us the strategy Pilate was going to follow for the day. Pilate's objective was to maintain peace and order in the city, and to do it at all cost, and he did not want to risk the possibility of a riot breaking out. His plan operated on several levels and directly involved three people: Herod, Barabbas, and Jesus. Pilate was certain that the Temple authorities, and Caiaphas in particular, were convinced that the Galilean was a serious threat to their authority, and that he must be put to death. Pilate was satisfied that the prisoner was enough of a threat to agree with the Jewish authorities that he must be executed.

For the first step Pilate wanted to involve Herod, who was in the city at that time. Pilate knew of Herod's access to Caesar Tiberius that dated back to Herod's student days in Rome and of his spying for the emperor on Roman soldiers in the colony. He didn't dare risk an unfavorable report by Herod to the emperor about his inept handling of an insurgent. So, when the Temple authorities brought Jesus to Pilate for a ruling, he planned to send him to Herod, since Jesus, a Galilean, came under Herod's jurisdiction. In this way, Herod would be forced to pass judgment on the prisoner.

Regardless of Herod's ruling, Pilate would require that the prisoner be returned to him for final disposition. When

the prisoner was brought before Pilate, he would ask him, "Do you claim to be King of the Jews?"

Pilate had every indication that Jesus would reply, "Yes," and that would be enough for Pilate to condemn him to death as a political agitator and insurgent.

Pilate then planned to invoke a practice used on major festival days in Rome, of executing major political prisoners so that the crowds might profit by the salutary example of the execution. In Pilate's plan, he would offer the crowd the choice between Barabbas or Jesus. He told Caiaphas of his intentions, and he was certain that the chief priest would send infiltrators into the crowd to incite them to call for Jesus' death.

At the same time, his spies among the Zealots were informed of the plan and it was expected they would drum up enthusiasm in the crowd to free Barabbas. The crowd's overwhelming call for the release of Barabbas would result in Jesus' execution and that would be the end of that. Of course, Pilate had no intention of freeing Barabbas, a known insurgent and murderer. Pilate's plan included having Barabbas killed while in prison, under the pretext of an unsuccessful attempt by Barabbas to lead a prison uprising. The plan would ingratiate Pilate with Caiaphas and the Temple authorities, give the rioting crowd something to cheer about, neutralize Herod, and get rid of two serious troublemakers, Jesus Barabbas and Jesus of Galilee.

Later that evening, when we learned the plan had been a complete success, one of the senior centurions remarked,

"It's hard to believe that Pilate thought it up himself. It's better than he usually does." I was eager to get away from the briefing room and to seek out Claudius whom I found in his room. I desperately wanted to talk with him about the events of the day, and to ask him more about the Galilean. "What do you think Jesus was trying to do?" I asked.

Claudius thought a long time, and finally moving his head from side to side, he said, "I don't know. It's really not clear to me." He went on to say that Jesus was very controversial, especially in his home territory of Galilee, where Claudius had followed Jesus' career very closely.

"Surely," I asked, "he must have known he'd attract attention by parading into Jerusalem and then carrying on as he did in the Temple? He seems to have a fine sense of drama. The parade he staged the other day was a perfect parody of Pilate's grand entrance into the city. With the colt for a stallion, the robes, the crowds and all."

"I don't think he was a fool, as some suggest," Claudius said. He said he thought Jesus knew exactly what he was doing. It wasn't always clear to others because of their own preconceptions.

"I'm certain that some of his close associates were convinced that he was a Zealot and that he planned to overthrow our army and set up the kingdom of Israel, and indeed become king of the Jews. Several of his followers were known Zealots." A Temple guard had reported to Jonathan that one of Jesus' followers, a man named Judas, called Iscariot, told him that he deserted the group

when he realized that Jesus was, in fact, not a Zealot and had no intention of leading a rebellion against the Roman army.

"If he wasn't a Zealot or a king, then what was he?" I asked.

Claudius said his information was sketchy. But he said he thought Jesus genuinely believed he was ushering in a truly new kind of kingdom; not a national theocracy, like Zealots were fighting for, nor did he mean to take control of some section of territory, like Galilee or Judea.

"His notion of kingdom," Claudius thought, "was not so much a specific place; its everyplace; its every place we know, from Rome in the west or even beyond to the Pyrenees and east of Antioch. Jesus was not content to set out a philosophy or idea which would be one among so many others, like a sect. His was a universalism that was not only intensive, that is, commanding, compelling, it was also extensive, inclusive, it embraces everyone."

His diety, Claudius continued, embraces Jews and Gentiles, Greek and Egyptians. He claimed his God not only created us all and therefore we are all somehow related to one another. But, his God demands that we treat one another as if we live in one large family. No, it's not as if we do, it is because we *do* live in one family. "Kingdom" for him means some kind of new universal order.

We speculated about this unusual man on into the night.

✠

During the return march to Caesarea I was under great stress. I knew I had to make a major change in my life — I couldn't continue, half-Roman soldier and half-Jewish believer. On the one hand I had found in Judaism some inner strength in accepting the belief in one God, and I had gained personal satisfaction in sharing some of my goods with others. On the other hand, my military assignments prevented me from observing the Sabbath rest and the dietary laws. I still felt unfulfilled and unsettled.

I hadn't returned to Caesarea for more than a few days when word came to headquarters that some disturbances had broken out again in Jerusalem between the Temple authorities and some followers of Jesus. There were charges and countercharges, arrests, and executions Members of the Caesarean synagogue followed the events closely, fearful that the unrest in Jerusalem might spill over into Caesarea and upset the delicate relationship they had achieved with the local Roman authorities. I must say I shared their discomfort.

One issue seemed to be the whereabouts of Jesus. His followers claimed he was alive; that he had risen from the dead. Others maintained his that Jesus' body was stolen from a tomb. But behind that dispute was another perplexing issue: Was Jesus the long-awaited messiah old Petronius warned us about? And if so, what did it mean for the Jews and their kingdom? Or the Roman empire?

But more personally, what did any of this have to do with me? If Jesus was the fulfillment of the promise of Judaism, what are the personal consequences for me?

If some of the Jews decided to lead an uprising against our forces, what would be my response? Defend Rome? Support Jesus? The turmoil raged for some weeks in the Jerusalem area; fortunately, it did not develop into a confrontation with the Roman troops nor did it boil over into Caesarea.

During these unsettling weeks, Claudius' cryptic advice frequently came into my mind: "Be careful!" I interpreted his remarks to mean that my best course of action for now was caution, not to make any major decisions at this time.

I used the time during this quiet spell to absorb myself in the writings of Isaiah under the direction of Rabbi Abram. Perhaps I did it as a distraction from facing the decision I knew I must make. I think I was attracted to Isaiah because I thought I saw some similarities between us. He, too, lived in troubled times and was in a position of some responsibility. His counsel, if heeded, might have profoundly affected the course of momentous events. In my own more modest way, I faced a similar circumstance.

I must say I pushed Abram to explain some of the prophet's writings that disturbed me. "As a professional soldier," I demanded of Abram, "what am I to make of this passage: 'Woe to those...who depend upon horses; Who put their trust in chariots because of their number, and in horsemen because of their combined power?'"

Or, who is the servant in the passage: "Here is my servant whom I uphold,...upon whom I have put my spirit; he shall bring forth justice to the nations....Until he estab-

lishes justice on the earth, the coastlands will wait for his teaching." Abram was a blessing to me during these weeks. He tolerated my outbursts and soothed my anxieties.

"Wait," he counseled, "Don't demand too much of God. God does the calling and places the demands upon those who can respond."

During this period something happened that profoundly affected the course of my life. Word came to the synagogue that one of Jesus' followers, a man named Philip, had returned to his home, here in Caesarea. He had left the city some time ago and settled in the Jerusalem area. More recently he became a close associate of Jesus' immediate corps of leaders, and the disturbances in that city caused him to leave.

That was fortuitous for me because I was able to spend long hours of study under Philip's direction. A major event occurred when he told me that Jesus' chief leader, Peter, was in Joppa and was willing to come up to Caesarea to meet with me. The speed of events seemed to take on a rapid escalation. My uncertainties and indecisions seemed to be swept away. For the first time, I decided to ignore Claudius' advice to be cautious. I was beyond caution and well on my way toward risk. I sent several of my men to ask Peter to come and tell me what I needed to know.

As I waited for Peter, I felt exhilaration at the prospects of meeting him. But at the same time, I experienced some discomfort. My old conflicts were not completely dispelled. What did the future hold for me, an officer in

Caesar's army and one of Jesus' followers? Was my life to become torn by contradictions? More importantly, were there conflicts between these two "ways" that I would be forced to resolve? Could they be resolved? ...

Afterword

Luke's two accounts of the meeting of Cornelius and Peter close the biblical record of Cornelius (Acts 10). According to tradition Cornelius became bishop of Caesarea, and his feast is celebrated on February 2 (Cath Bib Ency., NT, 157). His mentor, Philip, appears again many years later as Paul's host in Caesarea (Acts 21:7–9). The absence of any further reference to Cornelius suggests that this Roman pagan soldier turned Christian bishop had died prior to Paul's visit or had left the city. Also unrecorded is how Cornelius resolved any tension he may have experienced between his new profession of faith and his long-term career as a Roman soldier.

Resolution of Cornelius' tension may well have come within a few years of his meeting with Peter. A band of Samaritans marched on Mount Gerizim, about thirty miles north of Jerusalem, considered by Samaritans to be the most holy of all mountains. Pilate evidently construed the movement as an uprising against Roman rule and sent troops to put down the revolt, killing some and imprisoning others. It is not known whether the troops were from the garrison at Caesarea, or if so, whether they were

of Cornelius' unit, the Italica Cohort (Acts 10:1). In any case, if Cornelius remained in the Roman army for another thirty years, his dilemma must have become severe.

During the some thirty years after his meeting with Peter, Jewish nationalists repeatedly stirred up violent resistance to Roman rule. Finally, in A.D. 66, under Menahem, a descendant of Judas the Galilean, they revolted, drove the Roman troops out of Jerusalem and set up a revolutionary government. The rebels were counterattacked by other Jewish factions, resulting in a civil war. Roman armies finally crushed the revolt after four years of bitter fighting in which much of Jerusalem was devastated and the Temple was virtually destroyed. Two other Jewish revolts against Roman rule followed: one in 115 and another in 132. The latter ended with the Romans completely destroying Jerusalem. They literally plowed over the city and constructed a new Roman town on the ruins. Jews were excluded from the city; temples were dedicated to Roman gods and a shrine to Jupiter was erected over the site of the Jews' Temple.

The presence of Christians in the Roman army is much debated.[5] Justin Martyr, writing about a hundred years after Cornelius' conversion, claims Christians live in a new age with new demands upon them: "we who formerly killed one another, not only refuse to make war on our enemies but in order to avoid lying to our interrogators or deceiving them, we go freely to our death confessing Christ." Twenty-five years later, Athenagavas, in an open letter to the Roman emperor, says of Christians, "we have

learned not to return blow for blow...if they strike us on one side of the head, we have learned to offer the other...."

About this same time, late in the second century, written accounts indicate that Christians are numbered among the troops in a Roman campaign on the empire's northern frontier. The debate about Christians' involvement in warfare continued through the next decades. Clement of Alexandria, a noted theologian, did not appear to expect Christian soldiers to abandon their professions any more than he expected farmers or sailors to do so.

His pupil, Origen, a biblical scholar and theologian in the pre-Constantine era, objected strongly to Christians' involvement in warfare. For example, Origen related Isaiah's prophetic remarks to Jesus' active call: "For we no longer take up the sword against any nation, nor do we learn the art of war any more. Instead of following the traditions that made us 'strangers to the covenants' (Eph 2:12), we have become the sons of peace through Jesus our founder."

Thus, Cornelius' dilemma lives on.

Personal Reflections

"The Good Centurion" is a case study in the need for on-going conversion. The process of seeing reality in a new way, often times resisting it, creates a strong sense of tension that can be relentless. The words and example of Jesus do not let us rest if there is even the slightest openness to them. Those words and works require us to participate in bringing about God's reign. We are in constant need of conversion.

Questions for Group Discussion

- What struck you most about this chapter?

- What as it like to experience these important biblical events through the eyes of a Roman soldier? How is this different from your knowledge of the events?

- In this chapter, Cornelius portrays the Jewish people as powerless ("without choices or resources"). What segments of your community are similarly powerless?

- In what ways were you able to relate to the moral dilemma faced by Cornelius as he witnessed Pilate's abuse of power?

- Cornelius wondered what it would take "for Zacchaeus and other Jews to rise up and rebel." Have you

ever participated in any type of organized protest? Why? or Why not?

- Jesus cared so much about the people of Jerusalem that he wept over the thought of their eventual destruction. When have you ever been moved to tears from such compassion? How has compassion played a role in a conversion experience you have had?

- Jesus is described by Cornelius in some detail. What is *your* image of Jesus? Why do you have that image?

- Why was Jesus viewed to be such a threat by the Romans? As a follower of Christ, are you a threat to anyone in power? Why? or Why not?

- In a process of conversion where you experience much indecision and then you finally make a decision, what feelings do you have upon making that decision to change?

- Cornelius asked Claudius, "What do you think Jesus was trying to do?" What do you think Jesus was/is trying to do? What role are you called to play in that?

Son of Thunder

Foreword

The title of this story and the play on the word thunder in the account come from the treatment some writers give to the word Boanerges, a name given by Jesus to the apostles James and John (Mk 3:17).[1]

The details of James' narrative rest, with three exceptions, upon those provided in the Old and the New Testaments. The first two exceptions are details concerning Herod's affair with Herodias,[2] *and the reference to the beliefs of the Essenes.*[3]

The third exception is reflected in the section that deals with the history of the Pharisees. It is here that the Christian-Jewish dialogues spawned by the Second Vatican Council have been helpful. These dialogues have generated a serious exchange between Jewish and Christian biblical scholars and theologians that cast a new light on attitudes and information about the relationship of these two

great religions. For the purposes of developing Jesus' relationship to the Pharisaic movement in the storyline, these insights were invaluable.[4]

Some literary liberties were also taken: Peter's mother-in-law, left anonymous in Mk 1:22, is given the name Rachel (p. 65); the Pharisee who hosted a dinner for Jesus (Lk 4:1f) is named Jacob (p. 70); and the two messengers of John the Baptist are named Aaron and Saul (p. 84).

The old rabbi, Josiah, who taught James and John, is an added fiction (p.71), as are Jason, who deserted the group (p. 100); James' friend, Jude (p. 109); and Jude's friend, Isaac (p. 114).

The hymn James and his brother sing with their father is taken from Psalm 44 (p. 59).

The following is James' account of his experiences with Jesus.

In those early days with Jesus I felt a sense of pride to be associated with his companions and especially with him. But as his popularity grew, I became apprehensive. I could not define with certainty why I had joined Jesus' group in the first place. That may not even be the appropriate way to speak about it. I'm not sure I joined, perhaps I was called. But, if called, why me? And further, why did I say yes?

I know at the beginning there was a flush of excitement. Hundreds of us camped out on the banks of the Jordan

River with John the Baptist giving his rousing speeches. And then suddenly, one day Jesus joined us and he began to talk about the kingdom.

My initial attraction to him was the magnetism of his personality. I had never met, nor have I since met a person quite like him. When I try to describe him to others, as I am now, I find myself almost speechless. He seems to defy description. I can describe his height and his build. But it's his person that is elusive. He had a sense of personal composure that was extraordinary.

Jesus seemed to be in complete command of himself, so that when things went badly for us as they sometimes did, he was never perturbed. Not that he was aloof or unconcerned; quite the contrary. He was involved in the events, but he exhibited a confidence about the outcome, almost as though he knew what was going to happen. The events, however distressful for us, never seemed to upset him. And in the times when things went well, he was radiant. He laughed heartily and pranced about joyously with us to celebrate the good times.

I think, in part, my decision to join Jesus had to do with some sense of the history of Israel and the destiny of my people, because when we were young boys, my brother John and I often sat with our father for hours at the Bethsaida dock and listened to him tell stories about Israel's past glories. He often taught us to sing our ancient folk hymns. Those evenings were rich moments in my youth. Sometimes the Barjona brothers, Peter and Andrew joined us.

The stories we asked father to tell over and over again were about his adventures with two other Galileans who led an uprising against the Romans, Judas and Rabbi Sadduc. Sometimes other men and their sons joined us at the pier to hear these heroic tales. I recall the night one of the other men said to John and me, "Boys, back in those days we had a nickname for your father. We called him 'Thunder.'"

As I remember the stories, while father seemed to follow a general outline, the details from time to time received different embellishments. Sometimes he was one of Judas' lieutenants as they planned an assault of a Roman squadron. Other times it was he and Sadduc who carried out the exciting actions. Sometimes he digressed from the story line to tell us the exploits of our ancestors in their insurrection led by the Maccabees against the Syrians.

What I remember most about those evenings was how animated father became as he retold the stories. It was as if he took on new life—he seemed to be young again. The tales were about heroic deeds and courageous feats against enormous odds—the fully armed Roman troops and a few untrained, ill-equipped patriots fighting for their lives and the freedom of the people.

I didn't learn until some years later that father and his friends had in fact been defeated. As young boys we thought they had won the battles. I will never forget the night that I learned the truth. We were huddled in one of our boats and father was standing in the stern describing in graphic detail one of the dramatic scenes as he often did.

It had gotten quite late and mother came down to the dock to see what was keeping us. When she heard father regaling us with one of his old stories, she stopped him in the middle of a sentence.

"Zebedee," she said, "it's getting late. The boys should be in bed." "Just a minute, Salome," he said, "I have to finish this story."

"No! Zeb."

"Get home," he shouted. It was the first time we had ever heard or seen any sign of real anger between our parents.

"No, Zeb. The story *is* finished. It's over. It's been over for fifteen years. You and your rowdy friends didn't win. The truth is you lost. If you don't tell these boys the truth, they will grow up thinking the centurion's troops are here in town because they are our prisoners. You know and I know, and everybody in Galilee knows we are an occupied colony of the Roman Empire. We were then and we are now."

Mother turned and walked back off the pier toward our house, and father followed slowly behind her. When he began to sing one of the hymns he taught us, we joined in as well as we could:

"God, we heard with our own ears,
our ancestors have told us
of the deeds you performed in their days,
in the days long ago by your hand:
To put them in the land you dispossessed the nations,

you harried the peoples to make room for them;
it was not by their swords they won the land,
it was not by their arms they gained the victory;
it was your right hand, your arm
and the light of your face—because you loved them.
Wake up, Lord! Why are you asleep?
Awake! Do not abandon us for good.
Why do you hide your face,
and forget we are wretched and exploited now?
For we are bowed in the dust,
our bodies crushed to the ground.
Rise! Come to our help!
Redeem us for the sake of your love."

That evening was the last time father ever told us those stories, and we never asked about them again. Not that I never thought about them. The history of Israel was too rich to be forgotten and the biblical literature that recorded these events was so central to our religion and our way of life.

When we heard that John, who had baptized us, was in prison my apprehension about becoming a disciple of Jesus became acute. We knew Jesus and John were very close, so we were concerned about how Jesus would react to the news. But one thing was certain: John was a strong-willed person, with firm convictions. If he thought something was wrong, he said so, loud and clear. So none of us were sur-

prised to learn that John thought Herod's conduct was wrong. What was disturbing was the way John chose to make his feelings known. He went about Tiberias, in every forum he could find, publicly condemning Herod.

It was common knowledge throughout the region that during one of Herod's frequent trips to Rome he visited his brother, Philip, and became infatuated with his wife, Herodias. On Herod's return he brought her back with him to Tiberias to live in his palace as his wife. At the same time he sent his wife back to her father, King Aretas in Petra.

We learned the details of John's arrest from Joanna when she and her husband Chuza were in Capernaum visiting her parents. As Herod's chief steward, Chuza had access to the affairs of Herod's court, and he apparently shared these matters with Joanna. Because of her association with Jesus, which I must say I never understood, she confided them to us. She told us that Herod feared that John might arouse such a large following that it might lead to an uprising. She said Herod was compelled finally to imprison John after he was brought in for questioning. Joanna's recitation of the details confirmed John's forthrightness.

"What do you want from me?" Herod asked John.

"The question is not what I want. It's what is going to happen?" John said. "Unless you and the others change your ways, destruction is inevitable. So the question, King, is what do you want? Survival or destruction?"

Herod seemed fascinated by John's proposition, but he

was unable to know what to do. Finally, out of frustration, he demanded of John, "What do you want me to do?"

"You have insulted Aretas," John said, "and broken your alliance with him. The people are uneasy about this. But what is more important, you have broken our Law. You must give up Herodias."

"I cannot do that, and nothing you can do will make me do it."

"Yes, there is," John said. "I will continue to march up and down the roads of Tiberias and I will condemn your action to every one who will listen to me. The people will not tolerate your conduct."

"That's enough!" Herod said. "Take him away!" Herod ordered the guards to imprison John in the fortress at Machaerus.

After Joanna finished her account we all turned toward Jesus. Some moments passed in silence; my brother, John, was the first to speak. "We can't let him rot in Herod's jail. We must do something."

I agreed. "Let's go to Tiberias," I said, "and rally the Baptizer's allies and demand that Herod release him." The others were in agreement.

Jesus sat, silent; his head was down and his hands were in his lap. Finally, Peter broke the silence. Addressing Jesus, he asked, "Well?"

His head still bowed, Jesus said, "Well, what?" As he slowly raised his head, he continued, "You must see that Herod is not the problem. Herodias is not the problem, either. They are victims. They both bought Satan's prom-

ises. They think that with power and privilege they can control events. It's not true. I will never go to Tiberias."

"But what about John?" Peter asked.

"We have much work to do elsewhere," Jesus said. "So, let's get on with it."

✣

That night just before I slipped off to sleep, I asked John, "Where is all of this leading?"

John's reply hardly was reassuring: "I have no idea."

I found the answer in the events of the hectic days that followed.

A few days later several of us had been with Jesus in Magdala where he was teaching large crowds. We started out before dawn on the Sabbath to get to the synagogue in the Capernaum, where Jesus planned to continue his teaching. As we approached the town, Andrew complained about being hungry; Peter echoed the complaint. So Jesus led us through a grainfield on the outskirts of the town. As we passed through the field we plucked ears of grain, rubbed them together and ate them. As we came out of the field, a half dozen Pharisees, wearing their wide phylacteries and long tassels, were standing at the roadside.

"Why are you doing what is not lawful on the Sabbath?" one of them asked.

John shouted at them, "What are you doing here anyway?"

But Jesus quieted him. Many of the townspeople who

were on their way to the synagogue gathered around the Pharisees.

Jesus said, "Have you not read what David did when he and his men were hungry? They ate the bread of the offering which was not lawful for anyone but the priest to eat."

One of the Pharisees said, "What does that have to do with the question. David's men were outlaws. Are you saying that you and your crew are outlaws also?"

"No. I am saying we were hungry."

"No," a Pharisee said sternly, "I am saying you are breaking the Law. On the Sabbath you are forbidden to reap, thresh, winnow, or prepare food to eat. You and your men have broken the rules."

Jesus said, "What can I say to you? You have dozens of rules about what can or cannot be done on the Sabbath. God made the Sabbath day for us all. We are not made for the Sabbath."

"Come," Jesus turned to us, "we must go into the synagogue."

Jesus led us, with what I must say was a somewhat defiant pace, right passed the Pharisees, through the crowd and into the synagogue. As we moved through the crowd, John said to one of the Pharisees:

"If it is no crime to be hungry on the Sabbath, how can it be a crime to eat on the Sabbath?"

I was not prepared for what happened then. It all happened so rapidly, I'm not sure I can recall the events accurately. When Jesus finished preaching, the rabbi came

up to him and said, "You teach with such authority and command. Not at all like the scribes."

With that, a man in one of the rear seats who appeared to be possessed, broke out in a rage, raced up to Jesus and shouted, "What do you want with us? Have you come to destroy us? We follow the scribes. Have you come to destroy what we believe?"

Jesus said to him, "Be still; you are safe. Spirit, come out of this man!"

The man became calm and returned to his seat. Everyone was amazed. An old man, sitting next to me, said, "What's going on here? This friend of yours speaks with greater authority than the Temple scribes. Who is he?"

Before I could get my thoughts gathered to give the old man a sensible reply, Jesus came up to me and the others and hurried us out of the synagogue and on to the home of Rachel, Peter's mother-in-law, where he stayed when in Capernaum. As we walked along I realized how difficult was the old man's question. Beyond the fact that I knew Jesus was raised in Nazareth, I knew very little about him or his family. Some of us said he was John the Baptist or one of the prophets. But I could not have answered the man's question with any certainty.

A few weeks later another unsettling episode occurred. Jesus had been preaching in a nearby village when a person with leprosy came out of a thicket along the road and rushed toward Jesus. John and I tried to block the man's path without touching him.

Andrew shouted at him, "Leper, you must say, 'Un-

clean. Unclean.'" However, the man eluded us and ran up to Jesus, shouting, "Cure me. Make me clean."

Jesus, moved by the man's condition, shouted at us, "Don't try to stop him! Can't you see how he is suffering? Let him come to me." And Jesus touched the man and said, "Be clean," and he was cured.

I couldn't believe my eyes. He touched him! Jesus violated everything I had ever been taught. Leprosy is contagious and people with it were not to be touched; and only priests could preside over the cleansing. And Jesus touched him!

Peter rushed up to Jesus and said, "What are we going to do now? The man can get us into trouble with the priests."

Jesus said to Peter, "Don't worry." To the man he said, "Do not say anything about this to anyone except a priest. Tell him what has happened, and then make your offering according to the requirement of the Law to prove that you are cured. But do not say anything to anyone else. Do you understand?"

The man, beside himself with joy, said, "Yes, yes! I understand," and he ran off into the town. Within the next few hours he must have told everyone he saw about his cure, because the news spread so fast and so far that Jesus could no longer stay openly in the towns without being mobbed by the crowds. That wasn't so bad; the worse part was the man did tell a priest what Jesus had done, and that set some of the priests against Jesus.

It was then that we all agreed that it would be wise if

we disbanded for a while. John and I returned to our parents home in Bethsaida. Peter and Andrew also returned to Bethsaida. Jesus went out to some lonely place that only he knew about. Peter speculated that it was probably his favorite place, in the grove above Nazareth.

The few days that we spent at home were good for me. I had time to think about the events that had occurred during the weeks that I had been with Jesus. Certainly John's arrest was unsettling, but it was not altogether unexpected. Herod was always concerned about maintaining the delicate power balance between himself and the Romans. The troops billeted at the Roman garrison in Capernaum regularly patrolled the villages in Galilee to deter any unrest that might disturb the peace. When Herod decided to arrest John, rather than imprison him in Tiberias, he sent him to the remote region in Machaerus almost a hundred miles to the south. Jesus was right about Herod, he is a fox.

During the weeks we were together we did not have any run-ins with Herod's men or Roman soldiers. But because of the rumors about Herod's concern about Jesus, I felt a certain anxiety about the future. Jesus' actions contributed to my anxiety. Animosity seemed to build against him among some Pharisees, scribes, and Temple priests. On the one hand his actions toward persons in dire need were compassionate. I'll never forget the terrible disfigurement of the leper before Jesus cured him. But at the same time Jesus seemed to be deliberately, almost defiantly, provocative.

I was aware that he had a great following among the

people, especially those who were poor or impaired. However, the Baptizer had a large following also, and it didn't do him any good after Herod put him in jail.

During those days of reflection, I was not successful in quelling my anxieties. But I constantly recalled how reassuring Jesus' presence had been during those unsettling episodes. And while I was uneasy about the future, I looked forward to the time when our small group would reassemble, and I would be with Jesus again.

A few days later we reassembled in Capernaum at Rachel's home. Rachel felt a very special closeness to Jesus after he cured her of her serious fever. As the word was out that Jesus had returned, crowds of people swarmed around her house. I'll never forget Rachel's remark that day, "Oh, this Jesus. He saves me from the fever, only to have me trampled to death by his friends."

Among those who had crowded into the house were two scribes who introduced themselves as visitors from Jerusalem. While Jesus was talking to the people about the reign of God's kingdom, one of the scribes turned to me and asked, "Why does your master spend so much time with sinners?"

Jesus overheard the question, and he replied, "It is you who says I do. Do you say that persons who are blind or deaf or lame are sinners?"

"Of course," the scribes replied, "they sinned or their parents sinned before them. And God has punished them

for breaking the Law and only God can forgive them."
While they were talking a commotion broke out in the
room when some men, who were carrying someone on a
pallet who was paralyzed, forced their way through the
crowd and brought the man up to Jesus.

"My son," Jesus said, "your sins are forgiven."

That was the first time any of us heard Jesus say anything about forgiving sins. No one moved nor made a
sound. The room was like a tomb. The only thing I could
hear was the breathing of those who were crushed up
against me. I could feel my heart beating.

The scribes were outraged. One of them shouted at
Jesus, "You have no business talking like that. That is the
work of the Temple priests who can administer the rite
of forgiving the common penitents of their sins when the
priests receive a sin offering according to the Law. By what
authority do you say these things?"

The other scribe turned to the crowd and said, "It is
even worse than that. We have been taught that it is God
alone who forgives sins. This man commits blasphemy!"

People began to stir about. Jesus waited for them to settle down, and then he asked, directing his remarks to one
of the scribes, "Which is easier? To say to the paralyzed
one, 'Your sins are forgiven' or to say to him, 'Rise up and
walk'? I say both of these to him: You are forgiven and get
up and walk home."

The man began to stand up with help from several of
his friends. Then he straightened up and walked gingerly
toward the door with the people backing away to make

an opening for him. The people erupted in shouts of joy. The room emptied as quickly as it had filled, as the people raced out after the man and formed a joyful parade to his house.

The scribes were the last ones to leave Rachel's house. As they left, she said, "Good riddance."

One of them turned and said, "We'll be back."

Under my breath, I said to John, "Not too soon, I hope."

On a Sabbath, John and I accompanied Jesus to a dinner party at the house of Jacob, who was a friend of Jesus and one of the town's leading Pharisees. Among the guests were several other local Pharisees and some scribes visiting from Jerusalem. Two of the scribes had been at Rachel's home some weeks before.

During the meal one of the visitors from Jerusalem asked Jesus if he thought the Law of Moses was too strict.

Jesus said, "The purpose of the Law is to praise God and to care for one another. Otherwise a person who appears to be a servant of the Law may in fact become its slave. Isaiah said it well of such slaves, 'They honor me only with lip service, while their hearts are far from me. The worship they offer me is worthless. The doctrines they teach are only human regulations.' The truth is God's kingdom is in our midst now and it is for everyone so they may be fully alive; not to be slaves, but to be free. This truth makes you free."

"But," the scribe insisted, "we *do* have laws."

"Yes, we have God's law. But you have many legal codes and social practices," Jesus replied, "that are imposed by some for their benefit upon others who are victims."

The conversation was becoming heated when a man who had dropsy stopped outside Jacob's courtyard. We all could see that he was in severe pain. Jacob told a servant to send the man on his way, but Jesus interrupted,

"Wait. Can't you see, the man is in pain? Ask him to come in."

The man came in and said he wanted to see Jesus.

Jesus asked the guests, "What should we do with this man? It is against the Law to cure a man on the Sabbath. If he can be cured now should we want until tomorrow? It's only twenty-four hours. Surely one more day of suffering is not so bad, is it?"

Everyone was silent. I could not tell whether or not the silence came from shame, or guilt, or anger. My mind raced back to those days when John and I as young boys attended classes in the synagogue with the old rabbi, Josiah. "Remember," he often said, "keep the Sabbath. Whoever does any work on the Sabbath must be put to death." Our father never put out his nets on the Sabbath. It was a free day for us boys, and we played on the docks or roamed through the groves outside of town.

I didn't realize it at the time — it was years later that I recalled that servants of my father repaired damaged nets on some Sabbaths, especially during the season when the

fish were running. Even on this Sabbath day at Jacob's dinner, not everyone rested. While Jacob, his family, and we guests dined, servants brought food from the cooking area while other servants prepared the dishes. As I sat there thinking about what Jesus said about "legal codes and social patterns," he broke the silence.

"Please come here," he said to the man. He placed his hands on the victim's shoulders. "Go. You are cured."

The man ran out through the courtyard, ecstatic.

Then Jesus said to the guests, "Which of you, if your son fell into a well on the Sabbath would not pull him out without hesitation?" "Would you?" he said to one of the Jerusalem team. Turning to another guest, he asked, "What about you? Would anyone of you let your child drown while you waited for the Sabbath to pass?"

"You have no right," said one of the scribes, "to badger us like that. Who do you think you are?" Several of the guests appealed to Jacob to silence Jesus.

By then the spell of civility was broken. What began as a pleasant Sabbath afternoon dinner party disintegrated into an uncomfortable gathering. The party was over; pleasantries were quickly exchanged, and we departed. We later learned from Jacob that the Jerusalem team did not leave his house immediately. They were furious, and stayed on for some time discussing what they should do about Jesus. When they decided to include some Herodians in their plans, Jacob told them he did not want anything to do with their plottings.

✠

A few days later, Jesus asked Peter, John, and me to join him in the olive grove above Nazareth. I think Jesus spent the night in prayer. I can't say for certain, because while I stayed with him for some time, I frequently dozed off, as did the others. Some hours after dawn, he asked John to return to town and call the others to join us. When the twelve of us were all gathered together around him, Jesus said we were to be his companions, and that he would send us out to preach the Good News about the reign of God's kingdom. Jesus instructed us about many things that he wanted us to do and how we were to do them. We remained in the grove about a a week, praying and eating together and listening to him tell us of the wonders of the kingdom. It was truly a memorable week for us.

I must say I felt strange about the whole affair — a bit like the twelve sons of Jacob with each of us representing one of the tribes of Israel. It was as if we were launching a new Israel. We were filled with excitement and enthusiasm. I remember when we came down from the grove, I felt like racing into the village shouting about the kingdom at the top of my voice.

There were, however, several disquieting moments during the week. One was when Jesus related what must have been one of his most frustrating, and perhaps most frightening, experiences. He said it occurred some months before, here in his hometown of Nazareth. He had returned only a few days before from being with John at

the Jordan River. He and a group of the townspeople were gathered outside the synagogue after the Sabbath service at which Jesus had preached after reading a passage from Isaiah. The group's discussion broke into a dispute over a point Jesus had made. One of them challenged him: "Who do you think you are? Where did you get all this so-called wisdom, young man? Coming back here into town, parading as some wise prophet?"

Another man stepped forward and said, "I remember you as a young lad. You were a carpenter here in town with your father."

Someone else shouted, "We've heard about the great things you've done in other towns. What are you going to do for us!"

"I must say, I am amazed." Jesus said. "There is nothing I can do for you. You seem to think you need nothing."

"That's right," a town elder said, "we don't need you or anything else."

"May I say one thing?" Jesus asked, and without waiting for a reply, he continued, "You treat me like Elijah was treated. Like him, I must leave my home to do my work. In Elijah's time, a great famine left many widows in Israel. But God didn't send Elijah to them. Elijah was sent to the Gentiles where a widow gave him sanctuary, and he fed her and saved her dying son. And at another time when there were many people with leprosy in Israel, God sent Elisha to cleanse a Syrian army commander who was a pagan."

"What are you trying to tell us?" the elder asked.

Jesus replied, "You think you have everything, because

you think you own God. The God of our ancestors is not a tribal idol. You do not have God; God does not belong to you. You, in this town, and all the others in towns you have never seen nor heard of — Gentiles, Samaritans, Romans — belong to God."

"Not so, young man," the elder said. "God belongs to us. God made Gentiles to be fuel for the fires of hell."

The crowd became enraged. Several of the men grabbed Jesus, and hustled him up to the grove of trees on the hilltop overlooking Nazareth. While the men were talking about throwing him down the hillside, several of his disciples created some confusion and Jesus passed through the crowd and went on his way to Capernaum. I never heard Jesus talk about the episode again. It must surely have caused him great sorrow, because he had grown up with many of the people in that angry mob.

Jesus also told us, during one of these evenings, what happened to him in the days immediately after his baptism. "I knew," he said, "that I had to get away from everyone and everything. It was as if I was driven or led by a great force. I waded across the Jordan into the desolate region on the east bank, and I stayed there for days seeking guidance as to what I was called to do." He said the words of the psalmist often echoed in his ears, "You are my beloved son, with whom I am well pleased. Ask me, and I will make the nations your heritage and the ends of the earth your possessions. . . . I have put my Spirit upon you, you will bring forth justice to the nations."

"Were you there alone during this time?" Andrew asked.

"I think so, although at times I felt like I was being followed. But I never saw anyone."

Toward the last days in the desert, when he was weak from hunger, Jesus said he saw a great mound of stones and he thought, "If I am hungry, would God give me stones to eat?" He felt an energy surging through him that could empower him to turn the stones into bread, countless loaves of bread, enough to feed every person who is hungry. "With that power," he thought, "I can do the work of the prophet. I have seen hunger and have felt it, and I know that God is the source of the drive to eat to sustain life. The drive is almost compulsive; it can be overwhelming, even oppressive." Jesus recalled to us that the Scripture tells to what dreadful extremes people will go when they are driven by hunger.

The thought raced through his mind: "The one who will be their leader is the one who can feed them. Can I tell the stones to become bread? And if I can, what will be the result? Will people be more free; more human? To be human is more than merely to be well fed. Animals foraging in fertile forests are not hungry; nor are they human.

"After the stones are turned into bread, what then? What about thirst, and clothing, and shelter? Can I provide all of these needs with the wave of my hand? And if I do will people follow me? And if they do, what will become of them? Feed the hungry and they will make you king.

Prisoners are fed regularly, if not well, by their jailers. But food is not enough."

Jesus told us that that he concluded, "I will not resort to the role of caretaker. Bread is not enough."

Continuing his story, Jesus said, he came to a precipice, and saw, or thought he saw, the land stretching south to Egypt and beyond to the great sea to the west. He thought, "If I took the power to rule all the nations of the earth, I could fulfill the prophet's call: 'The rulers would kiss my feet and tremble when I waved my scepter, and then I could establish true justice on earth.' But if I took that kind of power, could I keep it? Would I want to keep the power? Might it be overpowering? To worship power is to be its slave." He recalled, "Yahweh is the God of power, there is no other. You must worship God and serve God alone."

"To seek to rule by force," Jesus asked us, "is that the way to lead people to freedom? Is that the Good News? Or is it not old news, as old as Pharaoh and Nebuchadnezzar, Herod, and Caesar?"

He recalled that a cloud then seemed to pass over him and he saw himself in Jerusalem, standing on the pinnacle of the Temple with the Kidron Valley hundreds of feet below him. A wave of vertigo swept over him, and he thought that if he were to leap into the valley, surely God would protect him, and all the people below would be amazed at his bravery and they would follow him as a great wonder worker. He resisted the urge when he remembered the wise guidance of the Torah: "Do not test God as the Israelites did when they asked, 'Is God among

us or not?' " When the ordeal in the desert was over, Jesus said he was physically exhausted, but he was relieved that the testing was finished, at least for the time being.

When we came down from the hilltop we found ourselves in the midst of controversy. Jacob told us that after his Sabbath dinner party the scribes and the Herodians failed to agree on a plan against Jesus, and the scribes returned to Jerusalem. But that wasn't the end of the matter. They reviewed Jesus' activities of the last months with the chief priests in Jerusalem, and decided that he was not a sufficient threat to get rid of him. Apparently the reports to the Roman authorities from the garrison at Capernaum confirmed this judgment. The plan, therefore, was to attack Jesus' integrity and discredit him before the people, rather than attack him physically. The plan almost succeeded.

It was clear that the Jerusalem scribes had returned to the region during our absence and had circulated rumors that Jesus was possessed by Satan; that he had lost his mind. In every town we visited, large crowds came out to meet Jesus, people from Judea and as far south as Idumea, east of the Jordan, and north to Tyre and Sidon. They just wanted to hear him or touch him. But at the same time, there were those in the crowd who would shout things like, "He is out of his mind," or "He is possessed, don't listen to him," or "He is a Samaritan." "A drunkard."

The rumors were so pervasive that by the time we re-

turned to Rachel's house in Capernaum, Jesus' relatives had hurried over from Nazareth to take him back with them. One of his cousins said to the crowd that had gathered about us, "He is beside himself. We have to get him out of here." When several of them came into the room and tried to seize him, John and I stepped in front of them. There again suddenly appeared in the crowds our "friends," the two Jerusalem scribes. One of them said, "He is possessed by Beelzebul. He casts out demons by the power of the prince of the demons."

In the midst of the commotion Jesus remained calm, and said, "You speak foolishly. You know that a kingdom torn by civil strife cannot last, as a family divided by loyalties cannot survive. If I cast out evil spirits — cure those who are sick and blind — by the power of the evil spirit, then Satan works against himself and his kingdom is doomed. But if it is by the Holy Spirit of God that I cast out demons, then the kingdom of God has come upon you. So, rejoice and be glad. The old divided kingdom is on the wane. God's kingdom is on the move."

Andrew then came into the room, made his way through the crowd to Jesus and whispered something to him.

Jesus said, "Speak up, Andrew, we have nothing to hide."

Andrew said, "Your mother and some of your relatives are outside, asking for you."

Jesus asked, "Who are my mother and my relatives?" Then he looked around at the people who sat about him,

and he said, "Here are my mother and my brothers and sisters! Whoever does the will of God is my brother, my sister, and my mother."

One of the scribes said: "Rabbi, you confuse me. One time you say you bring peace. Another time you say you do not bring peace. Which is it: peace or division?"

"As the kingdom comes," Jesus replied, "there will be troubled times. There are many false loyalties and social patterns that must be changed. And the change will be painful for some, and will cause divisions even within families. A household of five will be split three against two. The old patterns of the kingdom and those of the clan will not survive. The reign of God's kingdom calls for new social patterns. New wine cannot be held by old wineskins; it will burst the old dried leather. Some will insist, unfortunately, that the old wine is best."

That speech struck home. When John and I told father that we were going to join Jesus he said he didn't understand what we were doing or why we were doing it. John offered a reason: "It has to do with changing the way things are."

"What's wrong with the way things are, son? The fishing business we have with the Barjonas is good. Our fleet of boats is increasing. What's wrong?"

John caved in. "I don't know," he said, "but that's not enough."

"And you, James, what do you want?" he asked.

It was difficult to answer, because I knew that father had great plans for John and me to take over the business

and to see it continue to prosper. "I'm not sure that I can say it very well. But it has to do with what you have given us. You and mother have been good to us. It has been good here in Capernaum. It has been so good, perhaps, that we want to give some of it away." I knew I was losing ground when he asked, "Give what away?"

"It's not something I carry in my pocket. It's something you gave me that I carry inside me. I can't hold it in my hand, but I think I can share it with someone else."

"What is it?" he asked, almost with a note of desperation.

"Maybe," I said, "it's the love you and mother gave us."

"Salome," he said, "these boys are leaving us. I don't know why; I don't know where they are going, or when they will return, if ever. But we should have a good feast. They should have fish and lamb and wine, and our blessing."

I have often thought about that send-off we received and how fortunate John and I were. While our parents did not understand why we left them, our leaving did not cause a division within our family. Jesus was not so fortunate.

When Jesus finished his remarks about the breakup of families, an argument broke out among the people in the room. One of them came up to us and said to me: "You have been with this man for sometime, now. What does he mean about all this disruption among families?"

I said, "I think it has to do with listening to what Jesus says about the Good News of the coming of the kingdom.

Many of the old prejudices, old relationships, old restrictions will dissolve. And we will enjoy new ways of relating to each other. Our family squabbles will end. Patterns of domination by some over the lives of others will cease. It will be like the Exodus; all of us will be free."

From the expression in the man's eyes, he seemed to understand, and he said, "What do I have to do?"

Jesus, who was standing nearby, overheard the exchange, and he replied, "Come with us; follow me, now."

The man looked startled, and he said, "Oh, I couldn't do that. I can't leave now; I have too many family obligations, and business responsibilities. And I have...."

Jesus interrupted, "To be in the new kingdom, you must look to the future, not the past. You cannot enter the kingdom by walking backwards."

The man said, softly, "I can't go with you. Perhaps for me the old wine is best," and he walked out of the room.

As the crowd was dispersing, I asked one of the Jerusalem scribes what he planned to do. His reply: "We are not finished, if he is not."

"Do you think he is?" I asked.

"I hope so."

I felt like saying, "So do I." But instead, I said, "We'll see."

None of us was prepared for what happened at Caesarea Philippi; I certainly wasn't. We had encamped for a few days outside the town, when quite suddenly, one

evening Jesus said, "We must go to Jerusalem! We must begin now!"

I could not understand Jesus' note of urgency.

Later, John said to me, "What's gotten into him? Of course we're going to Jerusalem. It's Passover! We've all gone to Jerusalem since we were young boys. I've never missed a celebration in Jerusalem since I was twelve years old."

"Neither have I," I said.

"And neither has he. So why is he so anxious about *this* Passover?"

"Maybe something is wrong," I said. "I know he has seemed disturbed lately. But I'm not sure what it is."

Andrew, who rarely speculated about these things said, "What do you mean, you don't know what's bothering him? All of us know what it is."

Andrew was right; we all knew things were not going well. They hadn't been going well for some time. In fact, as the days went on, things got worse. Jacob had sent word to John, that there was a plot to kill Jesus. John was shocked; he couldn't believe it.

"Why in the world," John said to me, "would anyone want to kill Jesus? They must have mistaken him for someone else."

While I wasn't as certain as John, I didn't say anything.

I was still trying to sort out the events of the previous weeks when Jesus sent a shock wave through our group. One evening Thomas asked him, "Why do you have this urgency about going to Jerusalem this year?"

Jesus said, "I must go to the Holy City where I will be put to death by the ruling authorities. But I will rise again."

No one said a word. Peter stirred about, and tried to say something, but Jesus commanded him to be silent. I can't speak for the others, but I know I did not understand what he was saying. Frankly, I was afraid to ask him, because I feared what might be his explanation.

Shortly before we left for Jerusalem, Aaron and Saul caught up with us. We first met them months before when we were with John at the Jordan River. They told us that John had smuggled a message to them through a friendly prison guard at Machaerus, and they were to deliver it to Jesus. So we took them to him immediately. Jesus warmly greeted them and asked, "How is John?"

"Not good," Aaron replied, "he seems unsettled. He has heard about the things you have done. But he sent us to ask if you are the one who is to come or are we to wait for someone else?"

"I can understand why John is distressed," Jesus said. "But tell him what you have seen and heard: the blind see, the lame walk, lepers are cleansed, and the deaf hear, the dead are raised to life, the good news is proclaimed to the poor."

I was struck by Jesus' choice of words. The litany from Isaiah quite accurately described what he had been doing. But at other times Jesus chose other selections from Isaiah that included such phrases as "liberty to the captives, and freedom to those in prison." I turned to Peter, who was sitting beside me and asked him about this, and he said he

also had noticed the difference but he didn't think it was an appropriate time to raise the question.

Before I could pursue it any further, Jesus again spoke to our visitors. "Tell John one more thing," Jesus said. "Tell him not to lose faith in me."

Aaron said, "Oh, please do not misunderstand our mission. John believes. Oh, how he wants to believe. It is just that his confinement in the dungeon cell is becoming interminable. And he wants desperately to know...."

"I know. He wants to know," Jesus said, "how long he must stay in prison. As long as he stands on his ground which is firm, Herod will decide." Peter burst into the conversation. "Enough of this talk," he said, "You both must be tired after your trip. You must stay with us tonight and rest for your long journey back to Perea."

The next day, after Aaron and Saul left, Jesus said to us, "Why do you suppose people went out to see John when he was at the Jordan? Was it because he swayed like a reed in the wind? No. People wanted to hear his message, loud and clear. Did they expect to see someone dressed in fine clothes and living in the luxury of a king's palace? Of course not. John was dressed in robes like Elijah, and like Elijah he challenged the king. Now he rots in the king's dungeon. But long after the king is disgraced, John will be hailed as greater than the prophets."

A short time later a chill settled on our camp when we learned of John's death. It occurred during a lavish celebration of Herod's birthday with his courtiers, military

officers, and the leading men of Galilee gathered about him.

✠

Neither John nor I could recall which of us originally had the idea to talk to Jesus about our place with him in his kingdom. Yet we both remembered with vivid clarity our conversation with him and the argument that ensued. It was one of the most embarrassing moments of my life.

It began one evening after we left Caesarea Philippi. Several of us were comparing our experiences after we had returned from a tour of the towns in the vicinity. Jesus frequently sent us out in teams of two to tell the people about the coming of God's kingdom. The routine became very set. When we all reassembled Jesus would quiz us. Who did we see? What did we talk about? What was the people's response? What obstacles did we encounter? What did we do about them? What could we do to handle them better? As Jesus probed us, he would counsel us about how to do the work better. The sessions were very intense. After one of them, Peter told me that he thought Jesus was beset with the idea of training us to do his work after he's gone.

"Where's he going?" I asked.

"I don't know. But I think he wants to prevent what happened after the prophets died or were killed. They left no group behind them."

On this occasion some of us enjoyed greater success than the others. John and I received a warm welcome from the people of Cana. We met a great many townspeople in

the synagogue and held a number of house meetings. The people of Chorazin where Peter and Judas visited were less enthusiastic; some of them were downright hostile. Peter said that a rabbi denounced them one day in a synagogue, saying, "All of this kingdom talk can get you in trouble; and what's worse, it can get us all in trouble. I don't think Herod would find any of this talk to his liking."

Peter tried to reassure the rabbi by telling him that Herod would be welcome in the kingdom. Judas reinforced Peter by telling a parable he had heard Jesus use a number of times. The kingdom, Judas explained, is like a tiny mustard seed that grows into a large bush, and all the birds build their nests in its branches. "Like the birds in the branches," Judas said, "Herod would be welcome in the kingdom."

The rabbi snapped back, "Yes. But are you welcome in Herod's kingdom?"

Of course, we all knew that Herod was a man of great power and influence. He had several palatial residences, a large following of courtiers and he was on intimate terms with Roman military officers stationed in the region as well as the leading men of Galilee. It was also becoming clear to us that we might not be welcome in Herod's kingdom. The point was that this work of spreading the Good News was becoming dangerous and it was necessary for us to think about the personal consequences of continuing the work.

It was along these lines that John and I had been talking when we decided at our next opportunity, when Jesus was alone, to broach the subject. When the occasion was pre-

sented, I opened the conversation with, "Rabbi, we want to ask of you a special favor."

"What is it?" Jesus asked.

John spoke up, "When you are in your glory may we sit, one at your right hand and the other at your left?" John had not completed the question when Jesus began slowly to shake his head.

"You don't know what you asking," Jesus said. "Are you prepared to drink from the cup that I am to drink from?" Both of us said yes. Then Jesus asked, "Do you know that I must drink my cup in Jerusalem and will be handed over to the chief priests and scribes and to the Gentiles to be mocked and scourged and crucified? Do you know that?" Again, we both said yes. Then Jesus said, "We'll see," and he walked away.

Several of the others overheard our conversation and they confronted us. "What's all this talk about who is the greatest in the kingdom?" Peter asked.

Andrew said, "I was one of the first who followed Jesus."

John said, "That's right, and I was the other one."

Philip said indignantly, "What does that have to do with anything? What is important is which of us is the best?"

From that point on the discussion rapidly deteriorated into a loud argument that caught Jesus' attention.

"Enough of this talk," he said. "We have been through this before. I know that power can be alluring. I know because I have felt its allure, as I have told you before. To

have the power to force people to do your will, when you know you are right, is to be a supreme manipulator, not a leader."

Peter broke in: "We would never do that."

"Don't be so sure. I felt the allure of power again on the day I fed the throng that had been with us for three days. Seven loaves of bread and a few small fish fed thousands of hungry people. That's power! Don't think that I have not had moments when I have thought about what I could do with that power. Wipe out hunger and disease. Wipe away every pain. No more tears or death. But that is not the way it is to be for now."

Thomas interrupted, "When are you going to restore the kingdom of Israel?" "Be patient, and be on guard!" Jesus said. "For now, let me say, I know that you have stood loyally by me in my temptations. I, for my part, assign to you a place in my kingdom. But you must understand that power in God's kingdom is not as it is anywhere else. The domination practiced by political rulers is unacceptable in the coming kingdom. The Gentile rulers lord their power over people. But it is not to be that way with you. To esteem social rank and political power leads to pridefulness and arrogance and false feelings of superiority. All persons are great. Whoever wishes to be great among you must be your servant."

The discussion was over at least for the time being. But the fascination with power dies hard. This was not the last time the topic broke out in an argument among us.

The most embarrassing point about this episode in-

volved its retelling, which occurred more often that I like
to recall. Over time the details of the episode were embel-
lished to include my mother. One telling has it that she
took John and me up to Jesus and, she said to him, "Promise me that these sons of mine will sit at your side in your
kingdom."

One thing that had come through to me over the
months with Jesus, especially during the days when he led
us south to Jerusalem, was that he said repeatedly that
his mortal enemies were the elders, the scribes, the chief
priests, and the Roman authorities. I know that when he
said it I didn't fully understand why this was so; but I
accepted it at the time.

Then one evening, when Jesus and Peter were away,
Thomas jolted my complacency and that of the others
when he asked, with a note of exasperation, "I don't
understand; why Jesus is so angry with the Pharisees?"

Andrew corrected him: "Not *the* Pharisees; *some* Pharisees."

Thomas' irritation and the discussion that followed,
was sparked by Jesus' outbursts against some Pharisees
earlier in the day. "If the Temple authorities and the Romans are his greatest threat, as he says, what does he have
against *some* Pharisees?"

The irony was that many of us, including Jesus, had
good friends and allies who were Pharisees. I'll never forget
that chilling night when several Pharisees came to John to

alert Jesus that Herod was intent upon killing him. During the tours we made in teams of two, we were often welcomed and hosted by Pharisees in towns we visited. Some of them were our advocates when their fellow Pharisees were in opposition to us.

During our previous visit to Jerusalem to celebrate the Passover, we met Nicodemus, one of the outstanding Pharisees in all of Palestine. He had invited Jesus to be his guest, and fortunately Jesus asked Peter, John, and me to accompany him. I must say, Nicodemus impressed me; he was without a doubt the richest and most influential person I ever met. At dinner that evening, he said he had heard some things that Jesus had said about the coming kingdom and he wanted to learn more.

It was at that dinner that we met a friend of the host, a wealthy man from Arimathea, named Joseph. We had a lively discussion about Jesus' teachings and those of the Pharisees. The evening was not marked by debate or polemics; we just exchanged points of view and shared ideas we held in common. It was a very pleasant evening. Later when John and I talked about the dinner, I think we both were touched by that allure of power that Jesus had talked about. Both Nicodemus and Joseph had power. They had the resources to make things happen. I remember as I dozed off to sleep that night thinking what would it take to get either of them to join us. Would we have to change, and by how much? Yet, I thought, if they joined us what changes would they have to make.

But back to the evening that Thomas expressed his

exasperation about Jesus' antagonism toward Pharisees. Thomas said, "While we know Jesus differs with the Sadducees, I have never heard him say a word against them. What's more, I have never heard him say a single word, for or against, the Essenes or the Zealots. So what about the Pharisees? How different are we from Pharisees? We pray with them in the synagogue. We worship Yahweh with them. We honor the Torah and the writings of the prophets. We observe the high feasts, and we believe in the resurrection of the dead. We probably have more in common with them than with anybody else in Palestine."

"I don't know about that," Simon said, "but I do know about the Zealots. I was one of them, you know, for some time. They are hotheaded nationalists who are set on running the Romans out of Palestine if they ever get enough support among the people."

Simon went on at great length to describe their tactics of terrorism and assassinations to achieve their ultimate goal of establishing a new kingdom of Israel, free of Roman domination or any foreign rule. "Their objective," he said, "is complete political independence."

We all accepted Simon's assessment of the Zealots. Privately, I often wondered about his motives, since I knew he came from a family who were members of the Zealot party. Simon also told that he had strong ties to the family. This was evident several months before, when he became very depressed after he learned that his two older brothers were killed in an unsuccessful attack on a Roman outpost near Jericho. However, I never questioned him about his

reasons for joining us. Jesus seemed satisfied and that was good enough for me.

After Simon's description of the Zealots, Nathanael contributed his knowledge of the Essenes. He reminded us that before he became associated with John the Baptist at Bethany, he spent a year as a postulate at the Essene monastery at Qumran. While they were very religious, he felt they had little in common with Jesus' teachings. They vowed to be obedient to their superiors, to hate sinners, to be ready to go into battle with the "sons of darkness," and to keep Essene teachings secret.

"Why did you leave the monastery?" Andrew asked. Nathanael said he found their exclusiveness and rigidity unsuited to him and when Jesus asked him to join him in Galilee he did so eagerly.

It was the Sadducees who were almost a complete mystery to us. "Which of us knows anything about them?" Thomas asked. We discovered that none of us had ever had any direct contact with a member of their party. Matthew said that before he joined us, he frequently hosted parties of tax collectors; and on some occasions property agents were included. These agents were stewards of Sadducees, who were wealthy landowners, many of whom were good friends of Herod.

I related some comments that had been made about Sadducees at Nicodemus' dinner party. Nicodemus said they were conservatives in that they accepted the Torah as the sole source of the Law, and for them it was unorthodox to engage in oral interpretations of the Torah

or to honor the writings of the prophets. They rejected belief in rewards or punishment after death. They had a close relationship with the Temple priesthood, especially the chief priests and were the dominant influence in the Sanhedrin.

The Arimathean, Joseph, corrected Nicodemus: "Conservative? Sadducees are downright reactionary. Their objective is to maintain the status quo and they will go to great lengths in order to do just that, including collaborate with the Roman authorities if necessary. They will cooperate with anybody to preserve the existing delicate power balance, and preserve their wealth and position of influence."

Our discussion had gone on for some time, when Thomas, who started the discussion in the first place, brought us back to his initial question, when again he asked, "What does Jesus have against Pharisees? Clearly, we have so much in common with them."

Philip, who hadn't said very much up to this point, entered the discussion, "Thomas," he said, "let me offer a conjecture." Philip recalled for us that political activism of Pharisees goes back to the days when the Maccabees led the rebellion against Syria. Some of the Pharisees forefathers, who for all their claims that they placed their trust in God and not in human effort, joined the revolution. During the battles they gained a reputation among the Syrians as warmongers.

He reminded us that about a hundred years ago, during the reign of Queen Alexandra, who succeeded to the

throne after the death of her husband, King Alexander, the dominant political power was in the hands of the Pharisees. A popular slogan at the time was, "Alexandra ruled the nation, but the Pharisees ruled Alexandra."

The allure of political power was too much for them. During Alexandra's short reign, the Pharisees' rule became oppressive, and their exercise of power, absolute. They convinced her to execute Alexander's chief counselor who had been instrumental in the crucifixion of hundreds of Pharisees who apparently were involved in an insurrection during the king's reign. They also pressed her to execute other political enemies, many of whom fled the region for fear of reprisals by Pharisees. They banished and recalled, released, or imprisoned at their will.

The Pharisees had retained their strong political position even during the early days of the reign of Herod the Great. They were able to refuse Herod's efforts to force them to express loyalty to Caesar. Rather than execute them for treason, which their actions could have provoked, he merely imposed upon them a fine. However, the Pharisees were so well positioned among the influential families of the court that the wife of one of Herod's brothers paid the fine.

"I had forgotten," Andrew said, "that the Pharisaic party has such a history of political activism and even palace intrigue. The ones we know don't bear any resemblance to their ancestors."

"That's right," Philip said, "the present Pharisees are a nonpolitical group whose chief concerns seems to be with

pious practices of believing Jews." We all knew that for them the focus is on such matters as the preservation of ritual purity about food, and observance of dietary laws and the Sabbath day. Political issues such as whether to pay taxes to Rome or how to know the messiah are not on their agenda.

Thomas asked, "What caused the change from political activists to religious pietists?"

"Well," Philip said, "that's what I'm coming to. We can't absolutely be certain, but as I said at the beginning, let me offer some speculations. I think the answer may be in the leadership of Hillel." Of course, we all knew the name. There was not a rabbi in Galilee who did not quote from Hillel's sayings. Not that they all agreed with everything he said. But he was clearly the most respected rabbi of the last century. His grandson, Gamaliel, is an outstanding teacher in Jerusalem.

"Hillel was a contemporary of Herod," Philip said, "and it was during this era that the Pharisees shifted from a strong political party with ambitions to control the governmental policies to a publicly harmless pietistic group." Philip went on to suggest that it appears that Hillel anticipated that in the political atmosphere of his time, dominated by a strong leader in Herod, and complicated by the growing presence of Roman rule, if Pharisees persisted in seeking political power, they would risk extinction. "Hillel knew the violent history the Pharisees suffered in pursuit of political power," Philip said, "and he believed that in a conflict with Herod, Pharisees would be wiped

out. We may fault him for his conclusion, but hardly for his intention."

The dominant characteristics of Hillel's school, Philip continued, were accommodation, conciliation, and political neutrality. So long as Rome did not interfere with their practices of piety and the Temple priests complied with the cultic prescriptions, Pharisees are content.

"What's your point?" Thomas asked.

Before Philip could respond, Matthew broke in, "I think I understand. You're saying, Pharisees over the last several hundred years have made great contributions to our religion. They promoted the development of synagogues so that all of us, however distant we may be from the Temple in Jerusalem, have our own local place of prayer. Pharisees spawned the evolution of rabbis who are close to the people and are students of the Law and the Word of God. They encouraged families to adapt some of the purity practices in their homes that had been exclusive to the Temple priests. In fact, it seems to me for the most part, our practice of Judaism owes a deep debt to Pharisees."

That was undoubtedly true. The contributions Pharisees made over the years to preserve the essence and vitality of Judaism against the influence of Greek culture and foreign political force was well known. Even their name, Pharisee, "the separated ones," is living testimony to the tenacity of their resistance against the powerful influences to sustain monotheism and our religious traditions associated with the Torah.

"You're getting close, Matthew," Philip said. "Let me suggest that the reason Jesus gets so upset with Pharisees," pausing to nod to Andrew, "*some* Pharisees, is because he loves them so much. For decades they have been a leaven for the faith of Judaism. His exasperation, if that is the proper word, is because he expects so much from them. Unfortunately, many Pharisees suffer from a kind of paralysis of fear. Their past experiences in public affairs have often been disastrous. So now they are fearful, and they have turned inward, focused on how pious their actions appear, rather than how liberating their initiatives could be."

"Perhaps their flaw, if I may say so," Andrew offered, "is in their failure to understand power and its allure. Their fear of the public arena appears to be so great that their retreat from it is almost as severe as the Essenes. The consequences are that the existing order is maintained by the ruling Temple authorities and the Roman military goes unchallenged."

Judas asked, "What does any of this have to do with us?"

Without the internal certitude that my words portrayed, I said, "I think I know! That's what Jesus has been talking about all along. While those social structures and cultural patterns go unchallenged, the overwhelming majority of people live in semiblindness, a kind of bondage, severely taxed into poverty. That's the good news Jesus has been preaching: free the people from this bondage."

"Isn't that what the Zealots are all about?" Simon asked.

"Not at all," I said, "They just want to get rid of the Romans and then they will run Palestine. There is no good news in that. It is an old, tired message that involves clubs and swords and chariots. His is a new message. Jesus wants us — all of us, everyone — to deal with one another in ways that will radically change patterns of social behavior. He wants us to tell people to treat one another differently than the ways we have grown up with.

"It's not just that we are to be good to each other. We have to be good to everyone. It's easy for me to like you, at least most of the time." I glanced at John. "It's quite another matter for me to like people I don't know. Or better still, some people I do know or at least have heard about. How else can you explain what he wants us to do with our enemies? Not hate them, or tolerate them, or simply ignore them. He says it is not enough that we not hold a grudge against our fellow Jews; he says we are to love everyone."

"Everyone?" Thomas asked.

"Everyone, he says. But even beyond that he reminded us that we have been taught we are to hate our enemies. He says, on the contrary, we are to love them."

Thomas stopped me before I could continue. "Wait a minute," he said. "You and I may be ready for that message, but how many others will respond to it?"

"That's part of the message," I said. "There is risk in this adventure. The prejudices we carry with us; the hatred that seeps into families lives; the drive for power that plays

on human foibles, all of those forces are in opposition to the Good News. And they can be deadly. But the good news is about life, the fullness of life. That's the message Jesus wants us to tell everyone we see."

It was a sad day when one of our companions, Jason, who had been with us for several months, decided to leave. He joined us when he and Simon left the Zealots. He was well liked, although he never seemed to be comfortable with us. His level of intensity was unsettling. He was deeply committed to the God of our ancestors. Perhaps that was his problem; he was too deeply committed, if that is the proper way to express it. He joined our company along with Simon, who was his closest friend in our group. In the months he was with us he was always insisting that Jesus tell him whether something was right or wrong.

What provoked him to leave, I believe, was an accumulation of events that started several days after we set out from Caesarea Philippi for Jerusalem to celebrate the Passover. As we moved southward through Galilee, Jesus was greeted with great exuberance by crowds of people, and he seemed to be in high spirits as he went about the villages talking about the reign of the kingdom of God. By the time we arrived at Salim, some twenty miles south of the Sea of Galilee, we still had plenty of time to get to Jerusalem for the Feast. It was at Salim that Galileans usually crossed the Jordan River to the east bank and then pro-

ceeded southward to just below the river's juncture with the Wadi Farah. Then we crossed back over the Jordan into Judea; thus by-passing Samaria.

The route on the west bank was better for travelers: more villages; a superior roadbed; more frequent guards for protection against bandits. The west bank roadway was part of the north-south trade route from Damascus south to Tiberias, Jericho, Jerusalem, Petra, and on to Egypt. But despite its advantages, the fact is, it went through Samaria!

To make the trip for the high feasts, every year families throughout Galilee assembled at the southern tip of the Sea of Galilee; my father was one of the leaders of these caravans. When we made the three-day trek south to Jerusalem, we always by-passed Samaria.

On one of those trips, when John and I were young boys, and the caravan was encamped on the east bank, John asked me, "Why do we always take the detour past Samaria?"

I am several years older than John, and when we were young he thought I knew everything worth knowing. So I said, "Don't you remember those stories father told us about Samaritans?" Those boyhood images flashed back into my mind: John and I in one of the docked boats and father on the pier describing in graphic details the exploits of the Maccabees in the revolution against the Syrians. Then father took off on a tirade against the Samaritans: "Here, we Jews are in the midst of a battle for our freedom and the Samaritan leader sent a message to the Syrian

king, saying 'Don't confuse us with your enemies. We are not Jews. We accept your pagan god.' "

"Can you imagine," father shouted, "Jews denying they are Jews? But not only did they refuse to join in the fight for liberation, they fought on the other side. Romans are pagans! Samaritans are pigs! Samaria is poisoned!" A guard from the Roman garrison, hearing the shouts, came down to the dock to inquire about the commotion.

After calming down, father went on to tell other episodes involving Samaritans. During the uprising against the Romans led by Judas the Galilean, a group of Samaritans desecrated the Temple when they slipped passed the night attendants and scattered bones about the Temple courtyard. "Samaritan land is poisoned; Samaritans are pigs, I tell you," father said.

I must say that to the best of my knowledge I don't believe I had ever seen or met a Samaritan and, furthermore, I did not intend to. That's the reason the episode at Salim was so upsetting. As we were preparing to set off for the east bank of the river, Jesus told us he had sent several of the disciples into Samaria the previous night to look for accommodations for us. He reported that their effort was unsuccessful.

Peter was the first to respond: "I don't understand! Why did you send them into Samaria?"

"I wanted to find some villagers who would welcome us and provide hospitality."

I can't recall who spoke up next, but the sound rapidly degenerated into cacophony of voices. "Why would we

want to go into Samaria?" Thomas asked. Another, "I'll never go in there." Another, "The only way I'd go is if someone bound me and dragged me in." Several of the others headed east, toward the river. John reminded us of what was written about Samaritans: "My whole being loathes pagan people; but Samaritans are not even people. They are degenerates."

"I cannot imagine," I added, "why you would want to go into Samaria; I don't want their hospitality. But the fact is they have rejected you and I don't want them to get away with that. We must do something in retaliation." There was a chorus of affirmations. John, recalling the dramatic action taken by Elijah when the pagan king, Ahaziah, tried to capture him, said, "Shall we call down the fire from heaven and destroy them as Elijah did?"

While we were shouting and arguing among ourselves Jesus retained his usual calm demeanor. Finally, he said, looking at John and me, "There you two go again with your claps of thunder. How long must I be with you for you to understand what is demanded of the reign of God? You are all convinced that the Samaritans have wronged you. How many times have they wronged you?" he asked.

Peter shouted out, "Countless times!"

"Have they asked you to forgive them?" Jesus asked.

"Not once," said Peter.

"How do you know? You never go to them; you never see them; you do not know them. You just hate them, as they hate you. But I tell you, you must love them. Love

your enemies and do good to those who hate you. Then you may be children of your heavenly Father who makes the sun rise on the good and the bad, and the rain to fall on the just and the unjust."

"If they came to us and asked for forgiveness," Peter said, "how often must I forgive? As many as seven times?"

Jesus answered, "Not seven times. Seventy-seven times."

Jesus continued, "Some of you have said, 'I will follow you wherever you go.' But you must remember that if you do, I will take you to some places you have never seen before. And you may hear some things you have never heard before. Such is the kingdom of God."

Most of us followed Jesus into Samaria with great reluctance. But Jason and several others crossed over to the river's east bank and journeyed on to another village. We reassembled in Jericho several days later.

It didn't get any easier for Jason after we arrived in Jericho. I can't say it got better for any of us, for that matter. A few hours after we were in town, a delegation of scribes sent by the Temple authorities stopped us. One of them stepped forward and addressing Jesus, said, "We have been told that you are the leader of a group of Galileans. We also understand that you are a very independent person, not beholden to anyone. You don't respect the position or opinion of people in authority."

Of all the names I had heard used in relation to Jesus,

this scribe was coming the closest of anyone to calling him a Zealot. I had the feeling that a trap was being set and I was right.

"Let me ask you," the scribe said, "Is it right to pay the census tax to Caesar?" A large crowd had gathered and I was certain that every one of them understood what was happening: a man, and perhaps his friends, was on trial for his life.

It was common knowledge that Zealots refused to pay Roman taxes. To do so they felt was a dishonor to God. The land occupied by Roman forces belongs to God, and it was given to the Jewish people. To pay taxes to pagan rulers violates God's plan and is blasphemy. For Jesus to say publicly, "It is wrong to pay the tax," places him — and us — in the camp of the Zealots and vulnerable to arrest and execution by the Romans.

Jesus said to his questioner, "Do you have a Roman coin?" One was handed to him, and he asked, "Whose image is this and what is the inscription?"

Without looking at the coin, the questioner answered, "It is Emperor Tiberius and the inscription reads 'Tiberius, son of the divine Augustus.'"

"You have Caesar's coins," Jesus said, "then you should repay to Caesar what belongs to him, and to God what belongs to God." The delegation did not wish to pursue the matter and they left us. But Jason, not satisfied with the reply, asked Jesus, "Why would you give anything to Caesar?"

"Not now, Jason, we will talk later," Jesus said, "but

not now." It was several days later before we took up Jason's question. The opportunity was provided when Jesus told a parable.

Nobody could tell a story better than Jesus. Some say he was good at it even as a young boy. They really weren't stories; they were parables. John and I had grown up with great storytellers — our old rabbi, Josiah, and our father. But Jesus was a master. I think it may have been his storytelling that got John and me to follow him.

Jesus' parables were like jewels wrapped in priceless silk ribbons. Each layer of wrapping had a value in itself. As the story unfolded we waited expectantly to find the hidden jewel. But as Thomas said, "The sparkle of the jewel can be too bright for some eyes." Such was the case when a young scribe asked Jesus what he had to do to gain eternal life. Jesus had been preaching to a large crowd that had gathered when the scribe stepped forward with his question.

Jesus replied, "Surely you know what the Law prescribes."

The scribe quoted from the Torah about the command to love God and to love one's neighbor.

Jesus' response was also from the Torah, "Do this," he said, "and you shall live."

The scribe pursued the debate, "Of course," he said, "even a small boy knows those answers. But the question is, who is my neighbor?"

Jesus launched into a parable, and the longer he wove the tale, the more animated the crowd became. Jesus said

a man on his way to Jericho was robbed and beaten by bandits and left wounded on the roadside. Then a Temple priest saw the victim in the ditch and crossed over to the other side of the roadway and went on his way. At this point, there were muffled sounds in the crowd.

An old man with laughter in his voice, said, "I think I can give you the priest's name; he is called Temple-tax."

Jesus said another passerby was a Levite who also saw the victim and crossed over to the other side. Someone in the crowd began to laugh; then several others joined in. Not loudly; it was the sound of nervous laughter. A man standing next to Thomas said, "I know that Levite. His name is Stoneheart!"

While some people were obviously enjoying the story, others found it offensive. Someone in the rear shouted, "What are you trying to do, make fun of the priests?" A woman near the front of the crowd took her child's hand, and turning away from Jesus said, "I'm not going to listen to this disrespectful talk. Who do you think you are?" Several others also began to drift away. The parable seemed to have touched a sensitive note with the crowd about their feelings toward the Temple priests and Levites.

The scribe, who was clearly not pleased with the details of the unfolding parable, interrupted Jesus: "Why have you chosen a priest and a Levite?"

Ignoring the interruptions, Jesus proceeded with the parable. A third traveler saw the victim and was moved with compassion. Jesus dragged out the details of the para-

ble. He had the traveler pour oil and wine on the victim's wounds and bandage them; set him on his animal and take him to an inn. The traveler stayed with him overnight and paid the innkeeper for his care, and left instructions that he would repay the innkeeper for any additional expenses. Then Jesus asked the scribe, "Which of these three, in your opinion, was neighbor to the victim?"

The scribe said, "The one who showed mercy."

From the small remaining crowd, there was a ripple of applause, perhaps as much for the scribe's answer, as for the third traveler's actions. Jesus said, "Go, do as he did." The scribe said, "Tell me, rabbi, you identified the first two travelers. Who was the third one?" Jesus answered, "He was a Samaritan."

I was shocked! John and I looked at each other in disbelief. Why did he say Samaritan? There were so many groups he could have named. He could have said Galilean, Arimathean, or Judean. But no, he said Samaritan, and I knew when he said it, we were in serious trouble. The attitude of the crowd shifted immediately from one of joviality to hostility. It was clear that some of the townspeople were angry. Several of them rushed at Jesus, and John and I stepped into their path. Fortunately, the scribe diverted their actions by becoming the voice for the crowd.

The scribe asked, "Who are you, rabbi? First you are disrespectful of our Temple priests. And then you insult us with this disreputable story about...." He paused, seeming to find another word, any word, rather than to say,

Samaritan. "...about *this* traveler. What are you trying to do? Who are you? What do you want?" There it was again, Herod's question, "What do you want?"

"No," Jesus said. "That's not the question. The question is, what do *you* want?"

✠

We had been in Jericho a few days, when quite unexpectedly, I met Jude, who I had not seen in years. We were very close as boys growing up in Bethsaida. Our fathers' boats shared the same docks where we often played for hours.

In those days, Jude never seemed to be satisfied with boats and nets, and what he called "smelly fish." I remember one year when our families went to Jerusalem to celebrate the Passover, Jude didn't want to leave the Holy City. He put up a terrible fuss with his parents. On the trip home I asked him why he wanted to stay in Jerusalem. He said, "I love the city. It is so exciting. What do you want to do, spend the rest of your life in leaky boats trawling for fish?"

A few years later he went to live in Damascus with an uncle who was a merchant, and I heard from him infrequently in the intervening years.

When we met in Jericho, we recognized each other at once. I must say, Jude was dressed in great finery, so much so that I was embarrassed by my coarse outfit. But it didn't seem to bother him. We were so glad to see each other we immediately embraced, and we began to talk so rapidly

that we finally had to stop for either of us to hear what the other was saying.

We went to his home, which was quite grand, where we had lunch. He asked about my brother and my parents, and I asked about his family. The conversation was brisk for sometime, when he asked, "What are you doing in Jericho?"

It's strange, but from the moment I saw Jude on the street that day, I anticipated this question with dread. What could I say? It was obvious that whatever Jude was doing in Jericho, he was doing it very well; the opulence of his surroundings was evidence of his success. What, indeed, was I doing?

"I am on my way to Jerusalem," I said.

"Of course, for the Passover. Why don't we go together? Stay here with me and then we can go up to Jerusalem in a day or two. I have a house there and we can have a grand time renewing old stories. And I want you to meet some of my friends. But, tell me, what have you been doing?" Again, I hesitated, and finally I found a word, "Traveling."

"Where have you been? To Alexandria? Antioch? Perhaps Rome? It is such an incredible city."

"Well, no. None of those places."

"Where?"

"Around the towns of Galilee."

"Oh," Jude said with a note of disappointment. I knew this line of conversation was doomed, so I said, "I've joined the company of a Galilean named Jesus."

There was a moment of silence. It was clear that Jude had no idea who I was talking about, but he seemed to be sincerely willing to give me the benefit of the doubt. So, he said, "Who is Jesus?"

Where to begin? Son of a carpenter? A prophet? Miracle worker? Preacher? Rabbi? I stumbled through a description of our small company, of our excursions into towns and villages around Galilee, all the while hoping Jude would interrupt with a confirming comment or question.

Finally, he said, "May I ask a question?"

"By all means," I replied.

"What do you do?" How do you make a living? I always thought that you and John would probably become the owners of the largest fishing fleet on the Galilean Sea. What *are* you doing?"

I shifted focus from describing who was in our group and where we had visited to talking about the kingdom the way Jesus talked about it. I talked about people who were poor, or lame, or had leprosy. I talked about the abuse of political power and the oppression of the patriarchy. I tried to talk about these things the way I had heard Jesus talk about them. But as I droned on, I felt I was losing Jude.

He confirmed my doubts when he said, "Old friend, I don't understand what you're talking about."

I tried again. "Jesus is the most extraordinary person I have ever met. He relates to others like no one I have ever known. When he meets you for the first time, you feel he has known you all your life. When he sees some

one in need, *he* is in need. It's not just that he feels sympathy for the person; *he* feels the person's need. When he sees a person who is hungry, *he* is hungry. Last year when we visited a debtor's prison, *he* was a prisoner. He didn't want to leave. One cold night up near Caesarea Philippi we saw a beggar in rags and Jesus began to shiver."

I didn't tell Jude about a discussion several of us had the previous night. Thomas had said, "There is one thing I don't understand. If Jesus really wants to do something great for Israel and mind you, I'm not sure that he does, why does he avoid people with power? No, that's not it. Why is he attracted to people without any power such as those who are poor or sick or crippled? The rabble? They can't do anything for him."

"Maybe that's the point," Matthew said, "I think he, and maybe we, can do something for them."

"But what?" asked Thomas. "And, more significantly, why?"

John said, "I think I have known him as well as any of us. I think it goes way back, back to his mother. I remember one day he said his mother taught him to always care about those who were left out. She had a way of singing songs about it. She made them up out of the Psalms and the Scripture. One of them that she taught him went something like this:

> "God my savior has shown might with his arm,
>   dispersed the arrogant of mind and heart.

He has thrown down the rulers from their thrones
    but lifted up the lowly.
The hungry he has filled with good things;
    the rich he has sent away empty."

I didn't tell Jude about that episode; it did not seem to me that he would understand.

"What does he want you to do?" Jude asked.

"I think he wants us to feel the pain that others suffer. He wants us to feel it so intensely that we will do something about it. When Jesus talks about the kingdom, it seems that it is a place that is pain-free. Not because there has never been any pain, but because in the presence of pain, people did something to remove it. When he thinks about pain and suffering and death, I know he weeps."

"How do you know?"

"I know. I've seen him."

"Can I meet him?"

"Are you sure you want to?"

"Yes."

"Why?"

Jude seemed embarrassed by the question. He said, "Indeed, why should I want to spend any time with this itinerant rabbi, with no synagogue, no status, no influential following. I do hope you will pardon my candor; I don't mean any personal slight to you, old friend. But I want to meet this Jesus of yours because I have a dreadful fear."

"What possibly frightens you?" I asked, as I looked about the grandeur of his residence.

"I am afraid to die," he said. "I have so much that I own, and besides, I have so many who are dependent upon me. Last month in Caesarea one of my closest associates, Isaac, was accidently killed by a runaway chariot. He left a widow and three daughters. She begged me to tell her what was to become of her and her children. I could not help but wonder what is to become of Isaac, who, when I last saw him, was so alive and so in love with life. I wanted so much to say to her, 'You're alive. But what about Isaac?' But I didn't say anything. I ask you, 'What about Isaac?' And, old friend, what about me? Can this Jesus of yours answer my questions?"

"I don't know. You'll have to ask him." I told him that Jesus was holding a public meeting that afternoon in the town square. "Do you want to go?" I asked.

After a long pause, Jude said, "Yes."

When we arrived at the meeting place, a crowd had gathered. I introduced Jesus to Jude as an old friend from Bethsaida. John made friendly signs of recognition although in fact he was quite young when Jude left for Damascus and scarcely knew him, certainly not as well as I did.

In Jude's typical style of directness, he asked Jesus, "What am I to do to gain eternal life?"

"You know the commandments. Obey them," was Jesus response.

"I obey them. I have since I was a young boy. Ask James, he's known me since we were children."

Jesus did not turn toward me, but kept his face turned toward Jude. "There is one thing left for you to do." Jesus said.

"What is that?" Jude asked.

"You say," Jesus said, "that you have observed the letter of the Law. You even have a witness here in James to that claim. You are a good man. But you have a very serious problem. You are afraid to live."

"You're wrong, Rabbi," Jude said. "I'm afraid to die."

"No. You're afraid to really live, because you are possessed by your possessions. They rule you! They control you! You are like a man who had a bountiful harvest and he could not sleep at night. He had nightmares about how he could store his riches. Tear down his old barns; build new and larger ones? How could he find a way to keep this harvest safe so he could eat and drink and be merry?"

"Did he ever find a way to do it?" Jude asked.

"No," Jesus said, "One night during one of his nightmares he died."

"I know," Jude said, "I have those nightmares, too. What shall I do?"

"There is one thing left for you," Jesus said. "Sell what you have, give the money to the poor. Then, come with us and follow me."

Jude's face became ashen. He stared at Jesus for some time. Then he turned toward me for a moment, and looked like he was about to say something. However, he did not

say a word. He just stood there motionless. Finally, he walked over to me, put his hand on my shoulder and said, "Old friend, I wish you well." He walked away and that was the last time I ever saw him.

As Jude walked away the crowd dispersed.

We hurriedly left that afternoon for the remote town of Ephraim, because some friends informed us of a rumor that the Jerusalem authorities planned to kill Jesus. During our short stay there it was obvious that Jesus was not satisfied with hiding. And finally he insisted that we must move on to Bethany.

Jason left us the evening that we reached Bethany. We were gathered in Lazarus' house when Jason burst into a rage and shouted, "You and those stories you tell! Parables, you call them. I call them puzzles. You confuse me with those tales. You say the kingdom is like this or it's like that. That's not what I need to know. I don't want to hear what the kingdom is like. I want to live in the kingdom, now!"

We were all stunned, and we looked at Jesus who seemed remarkably calm. After a long silence, Jesus said, "Jason, now is not the time. To build a kingdom takes time. Some may not be able to accept that."

"I don't think I can," Jason said. "You say we must pay taxes to Caesar. You say we must love Samaritans. You say we must give everything to the poor. You ask too much. I cannot pay tribute to a pagan ruler who claims he is divine.

I cannot love people who are despicable. I cannot wait for your kingdom to come."

"Then do what you must," Jesus said. "But know that I care about you, and what you do. If you leave us, go with my blessing."

Jason went to get his things, and Simon joined him to help him pack. Several days later we learned that he was killed outside of Jerusalem when a small band of Zealots attacked a squadron of Roman soldiers.

The next day, Joanna sent word to us that the Temple authorities had decided that Jesus posed a severe threat to the political stability of Palestine. The Romans were getting nervous about Jesus' activities and his following, and the authorities agreed he must be executed. Orders had been given that if anyone knew of Jesus' whereabouts, it was to be reported immediately, so that the authorities could arrest him. Joanna also warned us that Jesus' friend Lazarus was also in danger. That evening Jesus told us we should be prepared to march into Jerusalem the next day.

I slept fitfully that night; the phrase he used, "march into Jerusalem" kept ringing in my ears. As I tossed through the night, I thought about the future. I realized I had no clear idea what Jesus had in mind for us. The thought struck me that a condition of being with him was to keep looking toward the future with confidence in him and in the way he prescribed.

That's risky, of course. It's safer and perhaps easier, as the elder said, to prefer the old wine. However risky the venture might be, I kept coming back to the same point.

Jesus always did what the situation required. John and I often talked about the wild night on the sea in the midst of a storm, and how Jesus calmed it. We've laughed about how we dragged Peter, soaking wet, back into the boat after he tried to imitate Jesus' walk on the water. Or the times we faced hundreds of hungry people with only a few loaves of bread and a couple of fish, and he fed them all!

Jesus seemed to have a plan to get to the city — some kind of a march to Jerusalem. But what was unsettling, was that I had no idea what he expected to do after we entered the city gates. We had never talked about it. Maybe I was afraid to ask him. If he had told us his plans, what would I have done? I don't know.

The one thing I was certain about: he repeatedly said that his kingdom would not come about by use of violence. And our straggly group certainly had no military force. If the Romans closed the gates tomorrow before we entered the city, that would be the end of our march. There was nothing we could do about it. A thought that kept coming into my mind was Jesus' repeated teaching about the incredible, unorthodox way we were to relate to everyone: Samaritans, women, Gentiles, Roman soldiers. At the gate tomorrow, we are to love the soldiers?

As I finally slipped into feverish sleep, I recalled what he had often said: "After death, I will rise again!" This remark, as it turned out, sustained me during the tumultuous days that followed. My last thought before I lapsed into deep sleep was: "I don't understand; but I believe! . . . "

Afterword

The story of James, son of Zebedee, ends in the scriptural account of his brutal death by order of Agrippa I about ten years after Jesus' crucifixion (Acts 12:2). No record is available about the cause of James' execution. The Gospels cite incidents of James' impetuosity and Jesus' attempts to curb it. The violence of James' death suggests that the strain of thunder in his character was stronger than efforts to encourage his prudence. He enjoys the distinct honor to be the first among Jesus' immediate followers to suffer martyrdom. Clement of Alexandria related an episode associated with James' execution. Though the substance of the accusation is unnoted, his accuser was so impressed by James' courage during his trial that he repented of what he had done, declared himself a follower of Jesus, and was condemned to death with James.

By the time of James' execution two major political rulers, Pilate and Herod, had been removed from the scene. Pontius Pilate's tumultuous reign as governor of the Roman colony of Palestine ended in disgrace in the year 35 when he was ordered by the emperor, Tiberius, to return to Rome to give an account of his scandalous conduct. Little is known about his subsequent fate. Eusebius, Bishop of Caesarea (c. 300) reported that he committed suicide.

Herod, who executed John the Baptist and taunted Jesus during his arrest, had fatally destabilized his political alliance with the Nabataeans when he rejected his

first wife, the daughter of Aretas, king of the Nabataean Arabs. In a border dispute, Aretas' forces defeated Herod and he fell into disfavor with Roman imperial power. He and Herodias were exiled to Gaul and there is no further record of either of them.

Agrippa I, a grandson of Herod the Great, and heir of Herod Antipas, had secured the favor of the Roman emperor, Caligula, and he was given reign as king of Herod's territories in the year 40.

Personal Reflections

Following Jesus is a lifelong journey. It is unsettling but motivating. The path is always clear but, at times, we close our eyes to it and falsely claim that the way is foggy. Jesus was clear about the subtle distinction between rules (social practices and laws) that were made to enhance the dignity of people and ones that were oppressive. As followers, he calls us to understand and act on the same distinctions.

Questions for Group Discussion

- What struck you most about this chapter?

- What did James mean when he said he did not really "join" Jesus' group, but was "called"? How have you experienced a calling in your life?

- At one point, James says that Jesus violated everything he was taught. In what way is that true for you?

- Jesus claims that there are "many legal codes and social practices that are imposed by some for their benefit upon others who are victims." How do you feel about that? In what ways does that statement apply today in your own community?

- In what way do we act like the people of Nazareth, as if we "own" God, or that God belongs exclusively to us?

- John and James made the decision to follow Jesus knowing it was not going to be easy. What are some of the obstacles that keep you from a full commitment to following Christ?

- Jesus talked about and experienced the temptation of power. Yet, he was a very powerful leader. What is holy about power? What is evil about it? When have you witnessed each?

- A key lesson from the good Samaritan story is to challenge laws and leaders which either promote or ignore discrimination. How is that relevant today?

- Being a disciple of Christ, in Jesus' time, meant that one had to confront unjust laws and social practices. How is that true in our time?

- Following Jesus is a long journey, much like the journey to Jerusalem described by James. What gives you the strength to make that journey?

- James concludes his story with, "I don't understand, but I believe." What does this mean to you in your life?

Joanna's Story

Foreword

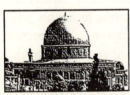 *For "Joanna's Story," Jeremias was a major source of encouragement as well as a source for many of the details. He laid down a challenge when he noted that "Only against the background of that time can we fully appreciate Jesus' attitude to women."[1] What, indeed, was the background? Here, as in the other two stories, sources for the events are the scriptural accounts themselves.[2]*

A number of present-day writers provided necessary details to document the pervasiveness of the existing patriarchal structure and the oppressive practices that discriminated against women during Jesus' time.[3]

Joanna's son, unnamed in the Scriptures, is given the name Josiah (p. 125). The anonymity of Peter's wife (p. 145) is removed by her being given the name Leah.

The episode about Susanna, the wife of Joakim

(p. 142), is adapted from Chapter 13 of the Book of Daniel.

Among the fictional characters added to the story are two of Joanna's friends, Miriam (p. 133) and Rhoda (p. 133), and Benjamin, a rabbi (p. 145).

Joanna's struggle with her sense of personal responsibility and social obligations follows.

When I was first asked to write my recollections about being with Jesus, I refused, because I understood I was being asked to write them from a woman's point of view, which seemed to be too narrow a perspective. When I asked, "Has a man been asked to do this from a male point of view?" the answer caused me to change my mind.

"Of course not," was the response. "It hasn't been necessary to make such a request. All of the recollections are from a male perspective. The biblical literature is dominantly written with a male bias."

So I reconsidered, and agreed to prepare these personal recollections of my time in Jesus' company. And I must say I am glad I decided to do it. I have found the experience extremely rewarding. Regardless of the value of these memoirs, which merely test my powers of remembering and my skill as a writer, what they did for me was to provoke rich memories of experiences that literally changed my life.

My relationship with Jesus began with two extraordinary events that were very nearly tragic. Chuza and I often visited my parents in Capernaum because it gave us a chance to get away from Tiberias and the hectic affairs of Herod's court. On one of the visits my son, Josiah, came down with a fever. This was the circumstance of our family's first encounter with Jesus.

In a few days his fever became so severe that we feared he might die. We tried everything we knew, but without success. Finally one of my mother's servants told me about the wonders a Nazarene named Jesus was performing for people in the region. When I told Chuza, he immediately sent several servants to locate this man. Word came back that Jesus was in Cana, and Chuza set out that day to find him.

Finding Jesus, Chuza burst into his host's home and appealed to Jesus to return immediately to Capernaum and heal Josiah.

"Just a moment," Jesus said. "I'm not a magician. Who are you, and what do you want from me?"

"Save my son."

"So many want to see signs and wonders before they will believe."

"I have been told you can cure my son."

"Do you believe I can?"

"Sir, cure him before he dies."

"You may go home; your son is cured."

✠

The day Josiah's fever broke, I had no idea whether or not Chuza had reached Jesus. In any case I was in absolute joy and I sent several of the servants to find Chuza and tell him the good news.

I must say that when Chuza returned to Capernaum he too was ecstatic as he told me about his meeting with Jesus and his promise to cure Josiah. It was indeed a joyous time when we three were reunited.

I never expected that any of us would see Jesus again or hear anything about him. But I was to learn the unexpected was characteristic of Jesus. The second event was also incredible. Several months later, I was again visiting my parents in Capernaum; Chuza was in Chorazin on business. I, too, came down with a severe fever. Fortunately, Jesus was in the town at the time, and my father took me to Rachel's home where Jesus often stayed when he was in the area.

"What do you want from me?" Jesus asked my father.

"You cured my grandson and I am eternally grateful to you. I know you can cure my daughter. Will you?"

Jesus, as he turned toward me, asked, "What do you want?"

"Please, cure me," I said.

"You are cured."

I could feel my fever break immediately. But it was not just that the fever passed and I became physically well. I felt strangely different about myself from what I had ever felt before. The full impact of this unusual feeling did not hit me until some time later.

My father thanked Jesus for what he had done and we hurried back to my parents' home. That night I could not get the experience of being with Jesus out of my mind; I was somewhat frightened. As I tried to sort out what had happened in the last several months, I thought of Josiah, myself, and Chuza. Each of us had experienced an incredible influence on our lives because of this man, Jesus.

❖

As I thought about my experience, I realized that it was not only the physical strengthening that my association with him had meant. It was deeper than that. I wanted to be with him again. At that time, I could not explain the reason for my attraction to him; I just knew that I had to see him again.

I knew it would be difficult to explain my feelings. It became evident very quickly when I tried to talk to my mother. "It's one thing to be cured of the fever," she said. "Thanks be to God. It's another thing to be interested in this strange Nazarene. What would Chuza say?"

"No, mother," I said, "it's not like that. It's not what you think."

"Then, what is it?" she asked.

I knew that would be her question. But even with the anticipation, I couldn't speak. Not because there wasn't anything to say. I was speechless because there was so much to say. Since my encounter with Jesus, my feelings toward Chuza and Josiah, my parents — everyone — were

deepened and enriched. So much so that I felt like I was living on a different level of intensity.

I think meeting Jesus fulfilled for me so much of what I had been feeling. I think perhaps it had begun when I was a young girl. One day in the synagogue, the rabbi read a selection from the Torah that struck me: "In the image of God, male and female God created them."

Later that day I said to my mother, "If we are created male and female in the likeness of God, then is God both male and female?"

"Joanna," my mother said, "don't bother your head about such things."

But I couldn't get it out of my mind. Those Sabbath services bore in oppressively on me. When the services ended, as my mother and I and the other women sat behind the lattice in the synagogue, we waited for the men to troop out. Then we were permitted to leave.

Chuza and I had a good life together. When we first met, Chuza was on his way to a successful career in Herod's court as a manager of one of the royal estates north of Capernaum. It was in circumstances associated with my father's winery that we met. He called on my father to conclude some business arrangements. Father owned many vineyards that supplied the region with choice wines, and Herod's court at Tiberias was a major customer.

Our families arranged our marriage, and both Chuza

and I accepted the social convention. Our marriage was blessed with a lovely son, Josiah, and our years together were rich and rewarding.

Chuza was a political man. He was from Nabatene and born in the capital city of Petra. When he talked about his hometown, which was not often, he referred to it in pleasant terms. He said, "It was a rose red city half as old as time. What it lacked in culture," he said, "it made up for in commerce." Nabataeans, Chuza claimed, were created to be inventors. "Philosophy," he said, "was for fools and those who had the luxury of plentiful rainfall. Only the fool did not take advantage of what he had."

I often listened, fascinated and unobserved, when Chuza, with pride, told Josiah about his native city and his ancestors. Petra, I learned, was built on the caravan route between Arabia and Syria and became a large commercial center. Nabataeans built numerous cities and fortified posts along these routes. Because they were poor in natural resources, but rich in strategic location, they developed diplomacy to a fine art. Early in their history they learned that to survive compromise and negotiations with forces more richly endowed was essential. Josiah was always impressed with Chuza's heroic tales about his forebears' episodes in support of the Maccabee brothers revolt against the Syrians.

The arrangement of the marriage of Aretas' daughter to Herod Antipas was precisely for this purpose: to secure stability of the political boundaries of the two peoples.

Herod Antipas' mother, the wife of Herod the Great, was also from Nabatene.

Water for Nabataeans was more precious than gold because the rainfall was so limited. They developed great skill in the design and construction of cisterns, dams, and canals. "Nabataeans had many gods," Chuza told Josiah, "but the two major deities were the one who controls rainfall and the one who invented diplomacy."

It was during the negotiations associated with Herod's marriage to the Nabataean princess that Chuza first came to Herod's attention. He was one of Aretas' principal negotiators and when the arrangements between the two courts were successfully concluded, Herod convinced Chuza to remain in Tiberias and take on special assignments for his court.

Chuza rarely spoke about his religious beliefs. He was raised, he said, with a range of fertility deities. The god, Hadad, dominated his recollections. "Hadad," he said, "was the storm god. He was pictured brandishing thunderbolts. As a child I feared him and at the same time I worshiped him. We believe that he controls the rainfall. And for us, rain is more precious than life. Without water life for us was a calamity."

A few weeks after my miraculous cure, I learned that a number of other women also were cured by Jesus. Through mutual friends I learned that one of the women, Mary, who lived in Magdala had suffered from a severe fever, and

she, too, had been cured by Jesus. So it was with great expectancy that I looked forward to meeting her and sharing our common experience.

I had the opportunity to meet Mary when I accompanied Chuza to Magdala on one of his business trips. The town had a thriving fishing industry in which Herod was heavily invested and Chuza frequently visited Herod's holdings.

After Mary and I met, we found that indeed we did have a great deal in common. We talked long hours for several nights about what we should do with our lives. Her father and her two brothers had died in a tragic boating accident, and Mary had inherited his prosperous fishing business. The care for her widowed mother weighed heavily on her, as did my concern for Chuza and Josiah. It was during one of these evenings that I confided to her about my childhood.

I told Mary that I never felt close to my father. I didn't fully realize it until Chuza and I had our son, Josiah. Father doted on him. Whenever they were together during our frequent visits to Capernaum or his to Tiberias, he showered the boy with attention and affection. I could not recall experiencing such intimacy with him.

I told Mary about an evening when I was a child, overhearing my parents in a heated discussion after I had gone to bed. Their voices were muffled and I could only occasionally make out what they were saying.

At one point, father's voice rose as he said, "I have a

great fear, Rebecca, that I am going to die before I have a son."

Mother said, "You fool. It could be worse. You might have had a stupid, foolish son who would bring great sorrow on your head."

"No," he said. "Such a son might be a disgrace but the birth of a daughter is a loss, in any case."

He took his fear to his grave since I was his only child.

On another evening, quite by accident I overheard father during his prayer session. "Blessed be God," he said, "that you have not made me a woman." I was dumbfounded. What was the meaning of the prayer? What did father mean? Did it truly reflect his feelings about mother and me? I wanted so desperately to talk to him about it. But I was afraid. Would he think I had intruded into his sacred moments and secret thoughts? What could I say to him that would not anger him? So I said nothing to anyone until the evening I told Mary.

One day shortly after my conversations with Mary, Jesus visited Mary's home. She had invited several women who knew Jesus, and she also asked Jesus to come up from Capernaum for the day. He greeted each of us individually, and as he passed among us he exchanged some special remembrance of our previous encounter with him. We then gathered around Jesus, he said, "Let us begin by reciting from the Shema." "Hear, O Israel," he began. "Yahweh our God is the one Yahweh. We will love our God with

all our hearts, with all our soul, with all our strength. Let these words be written on our heart. Repeat them to your children and say them whether at home, or walking about or at rest or at rising."

When we finished the prayer, Jesus turned to Miriam and said, "I noticed you seemed uneasy. Is there something you'd like to say?"

"Yes," Miriam replied. "It has to do with that prayer. I learned as a child that it was compulsory for men to pray Shema at specific times, in the morning, at noon and at evening." Others among us concurred with Miriam's comment.

Then she continued: "When I asked my mother why women were excused from saying the prayer at specified times, she said it was because the schedule of a woman in the household is subject to a timetable beyond her control. And for her to be bound to specific hours for prayer may interfere with the domestic demands placed upon her, especially by her husband."

Mary interjected: "It seems in the rivalry between God and a husband over a woman's obedience, God is less demanding. God can wait, with eternity available; a husband wants his meals on demand."

Mary's comment sparked another of the guests, Rhoda, who said, "That's not what concerns me. I find the synagogue service very depressing. We are told that Moses said we are all to gather together — the men, women, children, even the aliens in our midst — and listen to the reading of the Torah. But who among us has ever read the Torah to an

assembly? I have been told that women are not permitted to read aloud."

Jesus asked, "What reason was given?"

"I was told," she said, "that since women are inferior to men in all things, if a woman read the Torah in synagogue, it would cast a doubt on the piety and competence of the men of the congregation. I was told that surely there is a man among us who could read the selection and preserve the honor of the other men in the assembly."

"You have been told many things," Jesus said. "Some have said that fathers are to teach the Torah to their sons, but whoever teaches his daughter wastes his time. You have heard that a woman is not permitted to teach or to have authority over a man. She must be quiet."

Then Jesus said, "Let me ask you a question. Who do you say was the greatest person in the history of Israel?" We said the name Moses almost in unison. "Which of you," he asked, "can tell the story of what happened to Moses when he was an infant?"

There was a moment of hesitation, and then one after the other of us related the episode of Moses' mother, Jochebad, protecting her infant from the Pharaoh by hiding him among the reeds on a river bank. And then Miriam, his sister, convinced Pharaoh's daughter to save the child.

When we finished reciting the events, Jesus asked, "What did Moses do for the Jewish people?" Mary was the first to speak: "He freed us from captivity." Immediately, we all gave our assent.

"If Moses saved the people, who saved Moses?" Jesus asked. "Jochebad, his mother? Miriam, his sister? Or Pharaoh's daughter? If Moses was Israel's liberator, which of these three women saved Moses?"

None of us spoke. I was uncertain about Jesus' intention, so I said, "I don't understand. What are you asking of us?"

"I am simply saying, read the Torah and ask yourselves, 'What does it say?'"

I ventured an opinion. "The story of the infant Moses," I said, "seems to suggest that women had a role in the liberation of Israel."

Rhoda interjected, "That's not enough! Not just a role! To give birth to Moses would be an important role, but what Jochebad and Miriam did was play a significant, even a decisive, role in our history."

Mary offered, "What about Pharaoh's daughter? Can her role be ignored? It was critical."

None of us was prepared to deal with Mary's interjection.

Jesus said, "Remember the Torah says that God created them male and female and set *them* over all creation. Is there anything there that says one has domination over the other?"

"Are you saying," Mary asked, "that the system of male domination is ended, and is to be replaced by partnership?"

"In God's kingdom," Jesus replied, "we are all children

of God. There is not male and female; there is neither slave nor free person."

Jesus continued talking with us along this line for some time. Finally Mary said, "Let me tell you a story that I heard about what happened one day to Jesus in Tyre."

Jesus looked at Mary somewhat quizzically and asked, "Where did you hear about that?"

"Never mind," Mary replied. And she went on with the story. "Jesus had gone to Tyre with several others, Peter and Philip I believe, to get away for a while from the turmoil in Galilee. He didn't want anyone to know where he was, so he stayed in an inn on the outskirts of the city. But the seclusion didn't last very long. A woman, she was a Gentile, discovered Jesus' hiding place and stationed herself outside the inn, and refused to leave unless Jesus came out to talk to her. Her persistent appeal became so annoying that Philip, who had a way with Gentiles, went down to the street to quiet her. She began shouting so loudly that Philip and Peter pleaded with Jesus to tell her to go away."

"How did you get rid of the woman?" Rhoda asked.

"I talked to her," Jesus said, "and asked her what she wanted. She knelt at my feet and begged me to cure her tormented daughter. I told her that is not the reason I had come up to this territory. She persisted and said, 'Lord, help me. Cure my little daughter.'"

"Then what did you do?" I asked.

Before Jesus could answer, Mary broke in, and said, "Let me tell the story. Jesus attempted to rebuff the mother

by saying, 'I have come to feed the children of Israel first. It is not fair to take their food and throw it to the dogs.' But the woman replied immediately. 'Ah, sir,' she said, 'even the dogs under the table eat the children's scraps. I'll take crumbs. Please, cure my daughter.' "

Jesus picked up the story again. "I couldn't resist her persistent, convincing appeal. So I said, 'Go home, your daughter is cured.' After she left us alone, Peter said that woman's performance was disgraceful. No self-respecting Jewish woman would act like that.

"I said, 'Perhaps not. She certainly was not a silent, submissive woman.' "

Jesus said he reminded Peter that he had overlooked an important feature of the episode: "She changed my mind," Jesus said.

"You said that to Peter?" Rhoda asked.

"Yes, because it was true," Jesus said. "I had no intention of doing what I did when we went to Tyre. Or for that matter, even when the woman began her appeal."

"Then why did you do it?" I asked.

"Precisely because she spoke with conviction and she was persuasive. Let me ask you, if she had remained silent, would her daughter now be free of her torment? I had asked Philip and Peter to think about the courage it took for this woman first to confront them and then to stand up to me."

Jesus said that Peter was so distressed that he shouted, "These people are pagans!"

Then Jesus told us he asked Peter and Philip, "Do

you think God created this distraught woman and this tormented young girl?"

Neither of them answered. Jesus told them, "By this woman's persistence, she reminded me of a fundamental truth. I continue to grow in wisdom."

As the day came to a close, we all regretted that we could not continue our discussion with Jesus. He said to us, "I would like to ask you something. Will you join me and the others on my journey to Jerusalem for the Passover?"

"How is that possible?" Mary asked. "Women are not permitted to be in the company of men other than members of their family."

"You women are here today in my company."

"Yes, but this is a private meeting."

"Private or public, it is not relevant," Jesus replied. "I am inviting you to come with me to Jerusalem. I am asking you to come follow me because of the work I must do. I will need your assistance. Think about it. We can talk later."

And the meeting regrettably ended.

The episode of the woman in Tyre reminded me of the time several of us were with Jesus and he told us the story of a widow he had heard about who felt she had a just claim against the court. When she brought her case to the local judge he rebuffed her. For a long time he was unwilling to render a judgment in her favor, but she persisted in coming before him and pleading her cause. Finally he decided to render a decision for her be-

cause he didn't know any other way that he could get rid of her.

When he finished telling the story, Jesus asked us, "Do you think that the woman's actions were justified?"

"If her case was just as you say," Mary said, "I think she may have been too patient with the judge."

"Well," Rhoda said, "I'm not sure her conduct was justified. I don't believe a respectable Jewish woman should act that way."

"Do you think," Jesus asked Rhoda, "the judge would have ruled in her favor otherwise?"

"Doubtful," she responded.

"I see your point, Rhoda," Mary said. "You don't think the widow knew her place, whereas I think she did know her place. It was on the side of justice. It was the judge who was out of place."

During the next months some of us women accompanied Jesus and the others from one town and village to another as he announced the good news of God's kingdom. So many stories are told about Jesus and his association with women that they could fill volumes. I think one of my favorites is about the woman who was so badly crippled that she was unable to stand erect. When Jesus saw that she could not hold up her head, he said to Peter, "Who is this poor woman?"

After Peter inquired among the crowd, he said to Jesus, "No one knows her name, but I was told she

has been forced to bend over in this condition for many years."

"That's intolerable," Jesus said. As he hurried toward her, several of the men tried to stop him. He brushed passed them and reaching the woman, he placed his hands on her head and said, "You are free." She stood up erect at once and began to praise God for her blessing. Some of the men grumbled about Jesus' actions in not only talking to the woman, but even touching her, a stranger.

"Please, understand," Jesus said to them, "this woman carries on her shoulders the weight of a system that is so oppressive to women that they can scarcely hold up their heads. You must remember that she is a daughter of Abraham and Sarah, and she and her sisters must be set free."

When Jesus said this many of the men became angry, but others in the crowd rejoiced at what he had done. It was the only time I had ever heard a woman referred to as a daughter of Abraham and Sarah. On another occasion Jesus acknowledged that the men said they were descendants of Abraham; yet here before this gathering, Jesus specifically paid tribute to this woman as a daughter of Abraham and Sarah. Little wonder that some of the men in the crowd were upset.

It was not that Jesus only talked about new relationships between men and women, and that old social structures must go; he also acted out these new ways. I will never forget the incident when some men brought a woman to Jesus who they claimed was caught in the act

of committing adultery. One of her captors asked Jesus, "What do you say that we are to do with this woman?"

"What does the law say?" Jesus asked.

"Moses commanded us to stone such a woman."

"What do the Romans say?"

"They do not permit us to execute anyone."

"It seems that you have a problem. You want me to advise you to ignore Moses or defy the Romans. Is that what you want from me?"

No one responded.

"You say she was caught committing adultery? "Who do you say can commit adultery?" Jesus asked.

"A married woman," was the response.

"What about a man?"

"Oh, yes, of course, he commits adultery if he sleeps with another man's wife."

"What if the woman is unmarried?" Jesus asked.

"It is not adultery. Adultery is committed when one man sleeps with another man's wife; he violates the husband's property. It is against the law and they both must die."

"So," Jesus said, "you have here a married woman who you say was caught in the act of committing adultery." He then sat down on a stoop, leaned forward and began writing with his finger in the soft sand at his feet. He wrote "Aaron." Then wiped it out. Then, "Lucius" and wiped it out. Then, "Jacob," and again wiped it out.

One of the woman's captors asked, "What are you doing?"

"Writing names," Jesus replied. He went on writing more men's names in the sand and then wiping them out. Finally, he stood up and asked, "Which of you was there at the time the act was committed, and who was it that committed the act with this woman? What is the name of this man? Is it you?" He looked at another man, "Or you? Or you?" He scanned the men's faces in the crowd, repeating his indicting phrase, "Or you? Which of you should stand here with this woman? Which of you witnesses is prepared to throw the first stone."

He sat down and began again to write names on the ground. And as he wrote the men drifted away, led by the town elders. After they had all left, Jesus said to the woman, "They have all gone and none of them has condemned you. Neither do I condemn you. Go and do not sin again."

One evening, when I was visiting Rachel, Susanna came in tears. I knew, from what Rachel told me, that Susanna was the beautiful wife of Joakim, a wealthy landowner in a nearby village. Two of the village's elders had been appointed as judges, and because of Joakim's position, they frequently visited his home. During these visits the elders became passionately attracted to Susanna and they plotted a time and place to attack her.

One day they found Susanna alone in the garden. Unless she submitted to them, they insisted, they would claim they found her with a young man. She refused, and she

shouted so loudly that the servants came to see what had happened. When the elders told their stories, the servants were shocked. The chief servant said, "I am ashamed; nothing like this has ever happened in this household."

The next day a number of villagers gathered at Joakim's house, along with Susanna's parents, her children and all of her relatives. She noticed that Joakim was absent. One of the judges said, "Make her remove her veil," which she did.

The other judge said, "We saw Susanna lying with a young man. When we saw the crime we hurried toward them, but we were unable to catch the man. Susanna refused to tell his name. That is our testimony."

Susanna, in her defense said, "God knows these men have given false testimony against me. I am innocent of what they have accused me." She knew, of course, that it was hopeless, because a woman's testimony could not be accepted.

Since the two were elders of the people, and judges as well, the assembly believed them and condemned her to death. On hearing this several of her servants made a tumultuous scene, crying and screaming about Susanna's innocence. In the midst of the disturbance, her chief servant led her away from the crowd into the arms of her parents who were waiting outside the garden gate. Susanna was hurried away to Chorazin, where she hid for several weeks at the home of an aunt.

When Susanna told her story to us, she said, "I had no young lad like Daniel, in the Scriptures, to come to my res-

cue. I didn't even have my husband. Or so I thought at the time."

Weeks after the frightening event, Joakim sent word to Susanna that he never doubted her fidelity. And he asked her to forgive his cowardice. He feared the influence of the elders and what they could do to him and his business if he did not seem to rebuke her. He promised to send her a generous stipend monthly if she would not return to his house.

Susanna's life was in shambles and she knew it. Her choices were very limited: attempt to return to her husband, Joakim, and risk execution or at the least be ostracized by him. Or accept the nonperson role, living in hiding on her husband's subsidy. Her aunt tried to console her but with no success. She became distraught and drifted into a state of deep melancholia. It was during this trying period that Jesus' path crossed Susanna's. Her aunt learned of Jesus' expectant visit to Chorazin and she took Susanna to the town square on the appointed day.

She was among the many men and women Jesus touched and cured that day, but the experience was so enlivening that she insisted she wanted more than to be cured of her affliction.

"What do you want?" Jesus asked.

"I want to join with you in your work."

"Come," he said, "follow me."

Months before all of that occurred, a decision would have been difficult. No, she thought, not difficult. Impossible. Her life with Joakim had been so secure and

prosperous, that to accept Jesus' invitation would have been out of the question. But now she wasn't sure what she should do. The invitation was so simple. She had so little to lose. All that she once held so dear was lost to her now. To follow Jesus would be incredibly easy.

The three of us talked well into the night. The next day Susanna decided to join us.

I grew up with suppressed guilt about my feelings toward Judaism. I knew I loved the God of Israel and I honored God's Law. I loved my parents and I kept the Sabbath. I tried to be a good wife to Chuza and mother to Josiah. But I never felt that I had brought my religious beliefs into harmony with my feelings about myself as a person, and as a woman. It wasn't until I spent time with Jesus that this internal conflict was resolved. The resolution was painful for me and unfortunately for others who were close to me.

The first time I raised the subject in public was one evening at a dinner party at my parents' home. Chuza, again, was away on Herod's business. The guests included Jesus, Peter and his wife, Leah, Rabbi Benjamin, and two scribes and their wives. It was only later that I learned the scribes were from Jerusalem. After dinner we gathered around Jesus to hear him talk about God's kingdom.

Before Jesus could begin, Benjamin proceeded to expound about God's covenant with the people. He extolled the heroic episodes of Israel's history where God was true

to the promises made to Abraham and to his descendants, and how God came to Israel's aid in times of grave distress.

As Benjamin related these incidents, I became aware of the fact that although I had heard these stories many times, I now realized they almost always feature men in the heroic roles. Heroines like Judith and Esther were exceptions. There were either no women in these events or when they appeared they were unnamed, or more often than not they were treated as property or pawns. How often I had heard that after the great flood God blessed Noah and his sons, and said to them, "Be fruitful and multiply, and fill the earth." Not a word about Noah's wife or the wives of his sons, who surely had to play an essential role in repopulating the inundated land.

As I was thinking about these anonymous wives, my father's voice broke into my consciousness and I heard him say to the rabbi, "Benjamin, we the sons of Israel, are truly blessed people. Praise the God of Abraham, Isaac and Jacob!"

I thought to ask, "What about the God of Sarah, Rebekah and Rachel?" But I didn't speak up. I remained silent and I stored up more guilt about my lack of courage for not speaking out and at the same time I felt more guilt about the anger I had for my father's remark.

Then I thought about poor Sarah and Rachel. The Scripture is silent about the anguish and shame these women suffered as barren wives subjected to the social pressures that accepted a husband's freedom to have concubines to serve as surrogate mothers.

Meanwhile, Peter had picked up my father's exalted note about Israel. "I pray the day will come," he said, "when David's rule will again take over Palestine, and his kingdom will reign again." He went on about David's virtues, and as he did, I recalled that we knew a good deal about King David's military victories, as well as his wives and countless concubines. But we knew virtually nothing about the feelings of his daughter, Tamar.

Tamar's lustful half-brother Amnon raped her. When she told her brother, Absalom, he insisted that she remain silent to protect her attacker from public shame. When David finally learned of the crime he did nothing, because "he loved Amnon, his firstborn son." Scripture limits the description of the feelings of Tamar, David's *only* daughter, to one phrase: "She dwelt, a desolate woman, in Absalom's house."

As Peter droned on about David, I finally could not restrain myself any longer. I said to him, "Does that mean that our new king will have even more concubines than did David?"

Everyone in the room looked at me in dismay. I cannot say that I was surprised by their reaction. I, too, was shocked by my remark. I desperately wanted to take back what I had said. But at the same time I wanted to say so much more about what I had been feeling during the evening's conversation. I wanted to explain how I felt about the disregard in the Scriptures for women's feelings and their role in the life of Israel. But I couldn't speak. I knew I couldn't adequately explain my feelings. So, I

just sat there looking at the guests as they looked back at me.

Finally, from a most unexpected source, one of the scribes spoke up: "It is good that we have done away with concubinage. In the beginning it was needed. Is that not true, rabbi, to perpetuate our people, in cases where wives were barren? But such a precaution is not needed now."

While his remark was directed to the rabbi for professional affirmation, he turned to his wife, evidently seeking not only her assent to his proposition, but also perhaps some sign of her belief in his own fidelity.

Before Benjamin could respond, Leah surprisingly interjected. "Perhaps," she said, "adultery has replaced concubinage?"

The remark was offered more as a question than as a statement and the attention in the room, thankfully, shifted from me to Leah. I then realized that there was only one person in the room who was still looking at me. It was Jesus, and he had a slight smile on his face. Until that moment he had not said a word since we had finished our meal.

"Joanna," he said, still smiling, "you know and feel so much."

Then addressing the group, Jesus said, "If we are to talk about the kingdom, we cannot start with David. His time was long ago, but his ways as well as those of Moses, were not the ways in the beginning."

"What is that you say about Moses?" Benjamin asked.

"Let me explain," Jesus said. "We have long lived in a

patriarchal structure. The patriarch is king; the father of the house rules over all his possessions, including his wife. In the tradition of the elders, women are not counted."

"That's right," the rabbi said, and the men sounded their affirmation.

"No," Jesus said, "it is not right. While it is true that it is right for a patriarchy and that we have lived in such a structure for centuries, it is not right for God's kingdom."

"What's wrong with it?" the elder asked. "It was good enough for Moses," Benjamin added.

"Moses accepted it," said Jesus, "because of the hardness of our ancestors' hearts."

"What does that mean?" Leah asked.

I noticed Peter snapped around toward her with an irritated look on his face.

"Our ancestors were unteachable on this point," Jesus continued. "Patriarchy was the dominant structure in this region back beyond the time of Abraham. It prevailed in Egypt and in Babylon. It prevails today in Rome and Palestine; it is in our midst tonight. Patriarchy spreads throughout our society. It penetrates into the family, the community, commerce, and marriage. In everything we did or do, men are viewed as superior to women; sons are better than daughters; husbands dominate wives. These patterns are wrong. They are as ancient as sin. It was not so in God's plan. Remember what the Law says: God created men and women as equal. God's plan envisions partnerships, not patriarchy; men and women as equals, not dominants and subordinates."

The longer Jesus spoke the higher the level of agitation rose in the group. Peter and one of the scribes began squabbling over the correct interpretation of relevant sections of the Torah. My mother and Leah were arguing about the proper role of a wife in marriage. My father, one of the scribes and Benjamin, obviously greatly irritated by Jesus' remarks, left the room.

As father left, I heard him say, "I don't want to talk about this any more."

The rabbi said, "Nor do I."

Jesus came over to where I was seated. He sat down and asked me, "Are you sorry you brought up this matter in the first place?"

"No," I replied. "Though I am sorry it seems to have broken up the party. But the party is not important. What is important is that we must talk about the demands of the kingdom."

"Not only its demands," Jesus added, "but also its rewards. The kingdom demands that we acknowledge that as males and females we are equal in the eyes of God. And when we live in that way — all of us, men and women — will reap rewards that we cannot imagine."

After some time passed, my father returned and spoke boldly to Jesus. "I must say, young man, that I can accept many of your teachings. I can see why Joanna has been attracted to your ways. But, if I may, as one who is much older — though perhaps not as wise in some ways as you, can I give you some advice? Do not continue to preach this antipatriarchy drivel. Not only do I believe you

are wrong — but that aside — you will incur serious opposition from the leaders of Israel. And it may not stop there. To pursue this matter is to seek conflict and perhaps even your death. Remember, your life could be in danger."

"I am grateful," Jesus said, "for your concern about my future. But the coming of the reign of God is more important than my life. I ask you, sir: think about your life; think about the promises and rewards of the kingdom. Support your daughter; she is a wise and courageous woman."

Some weeks later several of us were with Jesus in a nearby town where he had been teaching about the kingdom. When we gathered together one evening in a home where we were staying, the subject of Herod's separation from his wife came up. Someone asked if Herod had divorced her. I said that rumor has it that he simply sent her back to her father's palace in Petra.

Earlier that day, Jesus had been asked about divorce, because it was a popular topic arising from Herod's affair. Jesus had left some of his disciples perplexed by his answers.

That evening Thomas asked Jesus, "If I understand what you said earlier today about divorce, would it not be better for a man not to marry in the first place?"

"Shall we discuss it?" Jesus asked.

"The Law is very clear," Peter said, "If a wife fails to please her husband because he finds some indecency about

her, he writes a bill of divorce, gives it to her and sends her out of his house."

"Unfortunately," Matthew said, "it's not as clear as you seem to think, Peter. The question that is currently under dispute is what is the meaning of the term, 'indecency.' " We all know, with the exception perhaps of Peter, the state of the public debate. The followers of Rabbi Hillel permit divorce for any fault that the husband finds in his wife. But the followers of Rabbi Shammai permit divorce only under the condition of adultery."

"Some of the Hillelites," Thomas said laughingly, "go so far as to say a husband can write a bill if his wife spoiled his food. Where do you draw the line?"

Finally, Leah was compelled to intervene, and asked, "What about the wife's consent?"

"What about it," Thomas asked.

"What if she refused to accept the bill?" Leah asked.

"I don't understand the question," Thomas replied, as he glanced around the room, seeking assent. "The question is not relevant. If the husband is dissatisfied, *he* registers the complaint in writing and that is the end of the matter."

I was appalled by Thomas' response. But at the same time I was impressed by the fact that I maintained my composure. I was about to burst in to support Leah when Jesus, who was silent during the conversation, interjected:

"May I offer an observation? What about a wife? What rights does she have?" The room was uncomfortably silent.

Thomas entered the breach, and asked, "Is it lawful for a husband to divorce his wife?"

"The answer is no," Jesus said. "May I ask you a question, Thomas?"

"Of course."

"Is it lawful for a wife to divorce her husband?"

"The question is out of order," Thomas replied. "Moses permitted the husband to write a bill of divorce against his wife. There is nothing in the Law about a wife's permission to write such a bill."

"That's true," Jesus said. "But I must say that in this respect the Law is flawed."

At that Peter began to choke, slowly and quietly, and then louder and more physically. When he finally became composed again, Jesus resumed.

"Moses adapted God's Law," he continued, "to our cultural and social prejudices. Our forebears think, as do you, men are superior to women. I tell you that it is not so. No, wait," he said, as he recognized the resentment welling among the men. "It was not so from the beginning. God made all human beings, male and female. Both are equal in the eyes of God. You have lived in a patriarchal structure in which the husband is viewed as the king of the household. His wife and his children, his servants and his oxen are under his domain. God's reign, which is here in our midst, calls for new relationships."

Some of the men began to grumble; some began to leave. Jesus anticipated their reaction, and stood up quickly and said, "Just a moment! You must recall that

God made us equal, male and female in the divine image. It is for this reason that the old patriarchal patterns must end. Both of the couple in marriage must leave their families, join together and create a new family unit. In the kingdom that is coming in our midst, the old patriarchal structure must end. The couple is no longer tied to his family or to hers. God joined them together in a new compact; and they belong to each other. No one, no law, no bill, no ruler can separate them."

Later, after Jesus retired to his room, some of us continued to discuss well into the night his teaching about marriage and divorce. When some of the men expressed vehemently their serious doubts about being able to accept Jesus' teaching, I also retired. I could hear their muffled sounds as they argued even after I left. The voices of Peter and Leah were especially loud on occasion.

I heard Peter say, "In the old days Sarah obeyed Abraham, calling him 'lord.' Leah, you are Sarah's daughter, so do likewise."

"No, Peter," Leah replied, "for the simple reason that you are not my lord. I have only one Lord, as you do: The Lord, Almighty God."

Later, I heard Peter remark loudly about Eve's weakness and Adam's strength. "The woman was deceived and sinned," he said. "Not Adam." When he made a reference to honoring Leah as a member of the weaker sex, Leah screamed.

"No, Peter! You do not honor me because of my weakness. According to Jesus, your honor to me, as mine to

you, is because we are both equal in God's eyes. One is not weaker, nor the other stronger. Peter, we are equal!"

As the squabble continued on into the late hours my last thoughts were about Jesus. He frequently referred to the first creation account in the Scriptures. But I never heard him cite the second account about Eden and the serpent and the fall.

Chuza knew, of course, that I had been meeting Jesus with some women in Magdala for a number of weeks, and he had not objected. While he never expressed any interest in Jesus' teachings or his activities, he did have great respect for him because of what he had done for Josiah and me.

The first time I told Chuza I was leaving for a few days to join Jesus and some other men and women on a tour of nearby villages, I was surprised by his reaction. Chuza said to me, "I don't mind what you do when you go out like that. I trust you, Joanna. I don't even mind that you give Jesus money to support his efforts. From what you've said he can certainly use it. All I ask is that you don't do anything to jeopardize my position here at Herod's court. The fact is, Herod has said he would like to meet Jesus and hear what he has to say. But, as you know, I have not pursued it. I do not want to be responsible for bringing the two of them together. Herod is a very insecure person and he can be dangerous in certain situations. You know what he did to the Baptizer."

The months passed and finally a week before the Passover, I told Chuza, "I plan to join some women and go with Jesus and his followers to Jerusalem for the Passover."

His initial reaction was silence. I knew from experience that the silence meant Chuza considered the subject was very serious, and deserved an appropriate response. Finally, he said, "I do not understand."

"I'm not sure that I do either," I said, "But I do know I must go with Jesus to Jerusalem."

"Why?" he asked.

I searched inside myself for an answer and as I did I could hear Chuza recite the reasons why I should not go. He said it would be dangerous for me on such a trip. "We won't be alone," I said, "Jesus and Peter and other men will be with us." Even as I said it, I knew I was setting up his next objection.

"What will people say?" he asked, almost pleading. "It would be scandalous," he said, "for you to be traveling on the road with a group of men."

While I was trying to compose a reasonable reply, Chuza pushed on.

"What about me?" he asked. "When this becomes widely known here in Tiberias I will be the laughing stock in the court. I can hear the courtiers now: 'There was a steward of the king's treasure who couldn't keep track of his own wife.' It's one thing to go off for a day or two to nearby villages but why would you want to do this foolish thing? It seems like such a selfish thing to do."

I knew I could not explain my intentions to him because I could not clearly account for them myself. The best I could do was to try to explain, at least in some meager way, what I was feeling.

"Chuza, I can't expect that you will understand; not because of any failing on your part. That responsibility is mine. Ever since I met Jesus, as I have said before, I feel differently about so many things. But please believe me, it has nothing to do with my feeling any less for you. On the contrary, my love for you is far richer now than before. For me to go with Jesus is not as if I am leaving you. I just know that future events can be for us even more enriching for our life together than anything we have experienced. I believe that events in Jerusalem could lead to something greater than either of us can imagine. The only thing I can add to what I have already said is, will you come with me?"

That thought came into my mind spontaneously at the very last moment, as I was saying the words. And though it was not my intention to do so, it clearly shocked Chuza. After some moments passed, he reacted:

"Absolutely not! It is out of the question. Herod is leaving for Jerusalem in two days and he expects me to go with him. And I expect you to go with me as we have in previous years. If you don't go with me, you're not to go out at all."

The night before I was to leave for Jerusalem I couldn't sleep. I was too upset, filled with mixed feelings. I knew

that I *had* to go and that I had decided I *would* go. But I also knew that my leaving might drastically change the relationship between Chuza and me. Something he said kept racing through my mind: "It seems like such a selfish thing to do."

Was I being selfish, I asked myself. Was I only thinking about myself, and ignoring Chuza's feelings and Josiah's needs? I turned the questions over and over in my mind as I tossed through the night, searching for some answers. Perhaps, I thought, my decision was indeed selfish. I knew deep down inside I wanted to be with Jesus again. At the same time, I knew I couldn't say that to Chuza. I knew I never adequately explained to my mother my feelings about being with Jesus. And as I searched for a way to understand my feelings, I became aware again, as I had before, of the reason for my feelings. Jesus was the only man I ever knew who seemed to be completely at ease in the presence of women. He was not intimidated by women; he was never on the defensive. I never felt that he was patronizing me or being condescending. He genuinely sought my ideas; I felt that he wanted me to be a partner in what he was doing.

As I thought more about it, though, I realized that Jesus was that way with everyone, men and women, and even children. To him, everyone seemed to be an equal. I remembered how compassionate he was to the woman the townsmen accused of adultery. But at the same time, he treated her accusers with tenderness and respect. Perhaps his great attraction was that he was disarming. That's it!

He made everyone feel that they did not have to hide behind any defenses. No one had to hide anything. They could drop their guards, their false posture of defense, and be free to be themselves.

Jesus radiated a sense of equanimity that filled a room, and like a fresh scent the air seemed clearer than air should be. He seemed to be in full command of himself and his own identity. Not like Herod's military commanders, intoxicated by their egos and their power. I think it was Susanna who said he seemed to be announcing a new kingdom, where men and women were called to relate to each other as equals before God and one another. He certainly had that effect on me. I have felt differently about myself since I came to know him; I feel so much more — what is the word? — *human*. I feel peaceful. And so I wanted to be with him again. But that line of thought brought me back full circle to where I started. I was leaving because of what I would get out of it. So, wasn't my leaving an act of selfishness?

Perhaps. But then it struck me. There was something else. I knew that over the months I was with Jesus and the other women I had gained a new sense about myself as a person. I noticed it especially in recent days with my father. He talked with me about things we never discussed before. He even asked me what I thought about mother and him moving to a new house in Tiberias. I couldn't believe it; he had never asked my opinion about anything, ever! I don't even remember what I said. But I know that during the time I was with Jesus I began to feel that I was not a pos-

session; that I didn't belong to my father, nor to Chuza. I was my own person created in the image of God. At first, it was a bit frightening. In one of the meetings in Magdala when I voiced my fear, Jesus said, "Don't be afraid. In the kingdom there is no slave or free; there is no male or female in God's eye."

Could I communicate some of what I had come to know and feel about myself to other women? What Jesus had done for me, I asked myself, could I do for other women? It was during this night of feverish sleep that I took encouragement from something I remembered he said to us one evening.

"I will not be with you much longer."

I think it was Miriam who interrupted him by asking, "Where are you going?"

"More about that later," Jesus replied. Then he continued his thought, "You will do greater things than I."

Finally, I slipped off into a fitful sleep. But I was awakened by something I recalled my father had said to Jesus. "Your life could be in danger." He had warned Jesus that he might be in danger if he continued to try to break the power structure. Was the structure so deeply ingrained that men would be so threatened as to violently attack the challenger? What about Chuza? Or Herod? Or my father? The authorities in Jerusalem? Even as the sleep slipped over me, I felt a sense of uncertainty about whether or not what I was planning to do would be good for us all, Chuza, my father and mother, even little Josiah. It was on that note of uncertainty mixed with hope that I finally

found the sufficient peace I needed to sleep through the night....

Afterword

The biblical account does not reveal whether Joanna went to Jerusalem with Chuza or with Jesus' "group." Her name appears only twice in the New Testament. Luke lists her among some women who accompanied Jesus and the Twelve (Lk 8:1–3). He also includes her name among the women, who after finding the empty tomb, tell the disciples what they have seen (Lk 24:10). Joanna's further absence from Luke's Acts of the Apostles leaves us to speculate about her actions after Jesus' resurrection.

A likely place for her name to reappear was in the episode following Jesus' Ascension. The apostles gathered in an upper room in the capital city "together with some women, and Mary the Mother of Jesus, and his brothers." (Acts 1:14). The account is silent about Joanna's presence. Perhaps she is among the unnamed women in Matthew's report about Calvary: "There were many women there, looking on from a distance, who had followed Jesus from Galilee, ministering to him. Among them was Mary Magdelene and Mary the mother of James and Joseph, and the mother of the sons of Zebedee" (Mt 27:55–56). Mark's account of the same event lists among the women, "Mary Magdelene, Mary the mother of the younger James and of Joses, and Salome. These women had followed him

when he was in Galilee and ministered to him. There was also many other women who had come up with him to Jerusalem" (Mk 15:40–41).

Joanna's apparent absence at Calvary might suggest that she (and perhaps, Chuza) decided it was too dangerous for her as a member of Herod's court to be so publicly identified with an alleged traitor. The episode at the tomb was more private, even secret, and therefore less subject to public disclosure. In any case, the record of Joanna's story ends when she and Mary are rebuffed by the apostles when the women describe the incredible events at Jesus' tomb. Consistent with the cultural mores of the times about a woman as a witness, their testimony "seemed like nonsense and [the men] did not believe them" (Lk 24:11).

Perhaps after those hectic and historic days in Jerusalem, Joanna and Chuza returned to the court at Tiberias and with Josiah took up their lives again. The events of the Passover week may have enriched their lives together more than anything they had previously experienced. Later, Luke picks up a thread of what may be evidence of Joanna's continued influence at the court. Luke tells us about a thriving church at Antioch of prophets and teachers. Among the church's leaders he lists "Manaen, who was a close friend of Herod the tetrarch" (Acts 13:1). However close Manaen's relationship with Herod may have been, it is likely that he would have had contact with the people of Herod's court. Perhaps Joanna played some part in his conversion to Jesus' way.

The spirit of Joanna is reflected in Acts, where "not a

*few of the prominent women" in Thessalonica became be-
lievers, as did "not a few of the influential Greek women"
in Beroea (Acts 17:4, 12). Elsewhere in Acts and in Paul's
letters the names of other Christian women are in promi-
nence. Among them are Dorcas (Acts 9:36–43), Lydia
(Acts 16:14), Damaris (Acts 17:34), Priscilla (Acts 18:2,
1 Cor 16:19), Phoebe (Rom 16:1, 2), Claudia (2 Tim
4:21), and Apphia (Phlm 2).*

Personal Reflections

Jesus was remarkable in his ability to cut through the layers of ethnicity, culture, and historic social influences that tint the lenses through which one views the world, especially other human beings. He truly saw and sees each person for who each is, a child of God. "Joanna's Story" challenges us to examine our prejudices, and appreciate the unique qualities each of us possesses as a child of God.

Questions for Group Discussion:

- What in this chapter most struck you?

- How did Joanna's life change, as she claims, as a result of her experience of Jesus? How has being a follower of Jesus changed your life?

- Joanna was at odds with those around her because of her desire to be near Jesus. Does you desire to follow Jesus ever cause you to be at odds with those around you? Why or why not?

- From what you can tell, how was Jesus influenced by his culture? How are you influenced by your culture?

- Jesus either ignored or challenged cultural norms that were unjust. What has been your experience when you did the same?

- What implications are there for you today in the statements: "In God's kingdom, we are all children of God. There is neither slave nor free person; there is not male and female"?

- Jesus told the story of a widow's dealings with an unjust judge. Why is it so difficult to be on the side of justice?

- Joanna expressed feelings of being abused, feelings of being respected, and feelings of having self-respect. How does it feel to be humiliated? To be respected? To have self-respect?

- It is easy to say "I am a Christian." It is difficult to be a follower of Christ. What cultural patterns present obstacles to being true followers of Christ?

- Many changes occur to the people around Joanna as she became empowered by her beliefs. When have you had a similar experience as a result of your own empowerment?

- How do we unwittingly participate in and perpetuate unjust social practices and cultural patterns?

- What responsibility do we have individually and as a community to address discrimination?

Postscripture

The community of believers that Jesus left behind to carry out his mission was at best a ragtag team: without schooling or skills (Acts 4:13); several fishermen whose loyalty and prudence were suspect; others drawn from the margins of Israel's society, including several "burnt-out" Zealots and one who followed the despicable profession of tax collector. Two have become prototypes of the non-hero: one whose name is equated with treachery, Judas; the other with skepticism, Thomas. The community included some women whose conduct was surely viewed as scandalous to their contemporaries. The task for such a group was indeed formidable: to usher in the reign of God.

While Jesus' preaching about the coming of the reign of God, frequently recorded by the Gospel writers (Mt 4:17; 10:7; 12:28; Mk 1:15; Lk 10:9; 11:20; 17:21) contained no timeline for its arrival, it has a note of immediacy. His prayer-instruction included a petition for the coming of the

kingdom, not some ethereal hereafter, but here (Mt 5:10; Lk 11:2) and now. Jesus left no clear plan of action to remove social maladies that were deeply embedded in the societal structures of his day, such as slavery or sexism, discrimination or imperialism.

The Ascension marked a fundamental shift for Jesus' followers; a shift from Jesus present as the charismatic leader to his sacramental and communal presence through the church. The immediate post-Easter accounts detail Christianity's radical attempts to institute social patterns it thought might reflect those of the kingdom (Acts 2:44–46; 4:34–36). Paul corrected the Christians in Rome about their errant obedience to dietary laws and rituals when he reminded them that the kingdom of God is not a matter of "correct" eating or drinking, but of justice and peace, and "joy in the holy Spirit....Let us then" he reminds them, "pursue what leads to peace and to building up one another" (Rom 14:17, 19).

During the first several centuries after Jesus' Ascension, writers in the Roman world into which Christians migrated, were confounded by their ways. Christians were called "atheist" because they disregarded the patriotic Roman gods. Their professed love for everyone, female, destitute, and criminals alike, was beyond anything known in the religious beliefs of Romans.[1] Most observers used such terms as a degenerate sort of cult or an obscure, secret association to describe Christianity. To Christians' claim that their founder was the Son of God, critics countered with the charge that Jesus was a magician, and the

practice of magic was a criminal offense in the Roman Empire.[2]

In recent times, efforts have been made to label Jesus as a social revolutionary.[3] For Hans Küng, "revolution" applies to the violent overthrow of the social order. While Küng attributes certain traits to Jesus as a social revolutionary, as opposed to a violent revolutionary, he concludes that Jesus is "more revolutionary than the revolutionaries."[4] The Zealots, the violent revolutionaries of Jesus' time, had a restricted frame of reference guided by their intense nationalism that motivated them to seek the violent overthrow of Caesar's rule of Israel. Jesus' vision was radically different: God's kingdom encompassed the whole world, "to the ends of the earth" (Acts 1:8).

John Pawlikowski's definition of revolution is helpful in this regard and points to the "revolutionary" quality of Jesus' mission. Revolution is a process whereby a class of society experiences a hope-filled alienation from oppressive structures, that leads to the creation of new social structures with greater equality in the social order. In this context, a revolutionary change in structure is preceded by a new consciousness among the members of the society about basic human values of dignity and self-respect. The consequence of this new consciousness alienates people from existing structures that deny these values and leads not to despair, but to efforts to replace the defective institutions with those more consonant with the new consciousness.[5]

Wilken supports this line of defining Jesus as a revolutionary. He cites the use of the term seditious ascribed to second-century Christians by their Roman critics. He notes that Christians were not revolutionary because they posed a military threat to the Roman Empire. Rather, their power was in creating a distinct social group that "held profane what the Romans held sacred, and permitted what others thought reprehensible." In this way Christianity was emerging as a counterculture that had the potential to be disruptive to the stability of the Roman Empire.[6]

This social-consciousness dimension of the revolutionary content of Jesus' message introduces a cautionary note to claims that personal transformation is the *sole* intent of Jesus' ministry. Not that he did not urge personal conversion; the question is, did his teachings have social consequences directed toward structural change? The purpose here is not to trace through the centuries the efforts of Jesus' followers to be faithful to the content of his kingdom-teaching; the trail is too extensive and circuitous.[7]

The intention is to uncover the link between personal conversion and social transformation in contemporary terms. The insight of Pope John XXIII is instructive. Resting firmly on the Church's social doctrine rooted in the papal legacy dating from Pope Leo XIII's social teachings, as well as modern political theory, Pope John's thought challenges both conventional social structures and cultural patterns. He stated that when persons become conscious of their rights, they likewise have the duty to claim those

rights, while others are obliged to acknowledge and respect them.[8]

Pope John Paul II, in his encyclical, "Social Concerns," notes approvingly that there are signs of a growing awareness of solidarity among the poor as they seek to defend and promote their human rights. "By virtue of her evangelical duty," the Holy Father said, "the Church is called to take her stand beside the poor..." in their pursuit of greater justice.[9]

When the Church at the level of its highest teaching authority states the need to pursue the transformation of the world and to root out structural injustice, its perception of reality is tested. No longer can the content of its teaching be limited to categories of private morality and interpersonal relationships. Issues of social justice are brought into focus that must consider cultural patterns, economic structures, and political life. The traditional emphasis on charity as the only appropriate response to persons in need is insufficient. During John Paul's historic visit to the United States in 1979, he said charitable endeavors are not enough because they fail to address the causes of poverty. He urged U.S. Catholics to search for structural causes of poverty and to work courageously for the changes that must be made.[10]

John Paul reminds us that "Everywhere and in all things, Christians must seek the justice characteristic of God's kingdom." As a guide, he presents the final judgment described by Jesus in Matthew's Gospel (25:31–46). John Paul poses the scene as the standard that "must

always be applied to human history, it must always be the measure for human acts as an essential outline for an examination of conscience." The measure, he says, is that "in the final analysis, Jesus will identify himself with the disinherited — the sick, the imprisoned, the hungry, the lonely."[11] The profound religious truth that can be drawn from this biblical image is that we find God in an encounter with others, especially with those who are poor, marginal, or alienated; it is in this dealing with the problems of poverty that human life is fulfilled.

To Jesus' contemporaries, who had some power and authority, his message was a challenge to change their ways and those of their society. In our time, the message carries the same compelling challenge.

Notes

Introduction

1. An interim report, prepared in advance of the 1987 Roman Synod on the Laity, disclosed that U.S. Catholics most often cited social services and charitable activities as appropriate expressions of their social ministry and rarely mentioned efforts toward social change. Also expressed was both their high regard for the U.S. bishops' pastoral letters on peace and the economy and their great uncertainty about how to put the church's social teachings into practice and why they should do so. "A Consultation with U.S. Lay People," *Origins* (April 2, 1987), pp. 729–31, 734.

2. Editorial, *U.S. Catholic* (October 1985), p. 2.

3. Michael Warren, "New Stage of Weekend Retreats," *Origins* (June 21, 1984), pp. 90–96.

4. William J. O'Malley, S.J., "Jesus, the Warm Fuzzy," *America* (March 15, 1986), pp. 204–6.

5. George Gallup, Jr. and Jim Castelli, *The American Catholic People* (New York: Doubleday, 1987), pp. 30–35.

6. See Richard J. Cassidy, *Jesus, Politics and Society* (Maryknoll, N.Y.: Orbis Books, 1979); John D. Crossan, *The Historical Jesus* (New York: HarperCollins, 1992); Hugo Echegaray, *The Practice of Jesus* (Maryknoll, N.Y.: Orbis Books, 1980); Sean Freyne, *The World of the New Testament* (Wilmington, Del.: Michael Glazier, 1980); John P. Meier, *A Marginal Jew* (New York: Doubleday, 1991); Albert Nolan, *Jesus Before Christianity* (Maryknoll, N.Y.: Orbis Books, 1985); Gerald O'Collins, *What are They Saying About Jesus* (Mahwah, N.J.: Paulist Press, 1977); Pheme Perkins, *Hearing the Parables of Jesus*

(Mahwah, N.J.: Paulist Press, 1981); Paul Steidl-Meier, S.J., *Social Justice Ministry* (New York: LeJacq, 1984); William M. Thompson *The Jesus Debate* (Mahwah, N.J.: Paulist Press, 1985); and John Howard Yoder, *The Politics of Jesus* (Grand Rapids, Mich.: Eerdmans, 1972).

7. Joachim Jeremias, *The Parables of Jesus,* (New York: Scribner's, 1972), p. 113.

8. Pheme Perkins, *Hearing the Parables of Jesus* (Mahwah, N.J.: Paulist Press, 1981), p. 3.

9. Perkins, "Will the Real Jesus Stand Up?" *U.S. Catholic* (October 1985), pp. 26–33.

10. Nolan, *Jesus Before Christianity,* p. 10.

11. The Gospel of Mark, the shortest of the Gospels, has a strong clear story line depicting Jesus' public life. It is considered by many as the first of the written Gospels. See New American Bible, New Testament (New York: Catholic Book Pub. Co., 1986), p. 67; Wilfred Harrington, O.P., *Mark* (Wilmington, Del.: Michael Glazier, 1985), pp. ix–xi; Gerard S. Sloyan, *The Gospel of St. Mark* (Collegeville, Minn.: Liturgical Press, 1960), p. 3.

The Good Centurion

1. Josephus, *Complete Works* (Grand Rapids, Mich.: Kregel, 1981), esp. pp. 321–2, 379, 470–81, 505–5, 556, 598.

2. See Richard J. Cassidy, *Jesus, Politics and Society* (Maryknoll, N.Y.: Orbis Books, 1979) for an assessment of Pilate by one of his contemporaries, pp. 94–95. For additional details of Roman army life, see, Michael Grant, *The Army of the Caesars* (New York: Scribner's, 1974), and G. R. Watson, *The Roman Soldier* (Ithaca, N.Y.: Cornel University Press, 1969). For Roman soldiers' religious attitudes, see Harold Mattingly *Christianity in the Roman Empire* (New York: W. W. Norton, 1967) and Donald Dudley, *Roman Society* (New York: Viking Penguin, 1970). Claudius' remarks about "Fate is our God," is a paraphrase of Pliny's observations, cited in Michael Grant *The World of Rome* (New York: New American Library, 1987), pp. 149–50. For insights about the responsibility of the Romans for Jesus' death, see, Ellis Rivkin, *What Crucified Jesus* (Nashville: Abingdon,

1984), pp. 113–24; and Cassidy, *Jesus, Politics and Society,* pp. 77–85; and Joseph A. Fitzmyer, S.J., *A Christological Catechism* (Mahwah, N.J.: Paulist Press, 1982), pp. 58–62.

3. Joachim Jeremias, *Jerusalem in the Time of Jesus* (Philadelphia: Fortress Press, 1975), esp. pp. 48–9, 73, 148–51, 163.

4. Edward H. Flannery, *The Anguish of the Jews* (Mahwah, N.J.: Paulist Press, 1985), pp. 14–24.

5. Ronald G. Musto, *The Catholic Peace Tradition* (Maryknoll, N.Y.: Orbis Books, 1986), pp. 31–45; Louis J. Swift, *The Early Fathers on War and Military Service* (Wilmington, Del.: Michael Glazier, 1983), pp. 32–79.

Son of Thunder

1. Harrington, *Mark,* pp. 42–43; John L. McKenzie, S.J., *Dictionary of the Bible* (Milwaukee: Bruce Pub., 1965), p. 100; Sloyan, *Gospel,* p. 33.

2. Josephus, p. 382.

3. Josephus, pp. 274, 377, 476.

4. For an enlightening description by a Jewish scholar of the history of the Pharisaic movement during Jesus' era, see, Jacob Neusner, *From Politics to Piety* (Englewood Cliffs, N.J: Prentice Hall, 1973), esp. pp. 41–78. For an informative analysis of Jesus' relationship to Phariseeism by a Jewish theologian, see Richard Cook, "Jesus and the Pharisees," *Journal of Ecumenical Studies* 15 (1978), pp. 441–60. Also see John T. Pawlikowski. O.S.M., *Christ in the Light of Christian-Jewish Dialogue* (Mahwah, N.J.: Paulist Press, 1982), esp. pp. 76–107; Eugene J. Fisher, et al., *Twenty Years of Jewish-Catholic Relations* (Mahwah, N.J.: Paulist Press, 1986); and Eugene J. Fisher, *Seminary Education and Christian-Jewish Relations* (Washington, D.C.: National Catholic Education Association, 1983) for extensive bibliography, pp. 67–78.

Joanna's Story

1. Jeremias, *Jerusalem,* pp. 375–6. For a similar view see, Elisabeth Schüssler Fiorenza, *In Memory of Her* (New York: Crossroad, 1987), p. 152: "Only when we place Jesus stories about women into the overall story of Jesus and his movement in Palestine are we able to recognize their subversive character."

2. See Mt 8:14–15; 15:21–28; Mk 5:22–43; 12:42–44; Lk 7:36–48; 10:38–42; 13:11–13; 24:1–10; Jn 4:7–29; 8:3–11; 20:14–18. For the joining of Joanna's husband, Chuza (Lk 8:3) with the episode of the curing of the royal official's son by Jesus (Jn 4:46), and Chuza's etymology, see McKenzie, p. 136. Also for Nabatean background, see McKenzie, p. 601.

3. For extension treatment about the laws and practices oppressive to women of Jesus' time, see Rachel Baile, *Women and Jewish Law* (New York: Schocken Books, 1984). Especially useful for providing background data, see Joyce Hollyday, "Voices Out of the Silence," Sojourners (June 1986); Francis J. Moloney, S.D.B., *Women First among the Faithful* (Notre Dame, Ind.: Ave Marie Press, 1986); Elisabeth Moltmann-Wendel, *The Women Around Jesus* (New York: Crossroad, 1987); Evelyn and Frank Stagg, Women in the World of Jesus (Philadelphia: Westminster Press, 1978); and Rachel C. Wahlberg, *Jesus According to a Woman* (Mahwah, N.J.: Paulist Press, 1986).

In part Joanna's personality is based on a reference in Moltmann-Wendel, p. 137, to a book by a French priest Jean Claude Barreau (*Les Mémoires de Jésus*). Barreau has Jesus describe Joanna as "a woman who knows what she wants, and she does not let anyone push her around. My disciples still cannot bear women treating them as equals, so it is not surprising that there were often vigorous quarrels."

Postscripture

1. Grant, *the World of Rome,* pp. 210–13.

2. Robert L. Wilken, *The Christians as the Romans Saw Them* (New Haven, Conn.: Yale University Press, 1984), p. 80.

3. See Oscar Cullmann, *Jesus and the Revolutionaries* (New York:

Harper & Row, 1970) and S. G. F. Brandon, *Jesus and the Zealots* (Manchester: Manchester University Press, 1967).

4. Hans Küng, *On Being a Christian* (New York: Doubleday, 1976), pp. 183–91.

5. Pawlikowski, "Jesus and the Revolutionaries," *The Christian Century* (Dec. 2, 1972), pp. 1237–41.

6. Wilken, pp. 119–20.

7. For extensive treatment of the early church, see Charles Avila, *Ownership: Early Christian Teaching* (Maryknoll, N.Y.: Orbis Books, 1983).

8. Pope John XXIII provides a summary statement in the contemporary setting of this phenomenon of the revolutionary consequences of "a new social consciousness" in "Pacem in Terris." See Joseph Gremillion, *The Gospel of Peace and Justice* (Maryknoll, N.Y.: Orbis Books, 1976), pp. 209–10.

"Our age has three distinctive characteristics. First of all, we note that the working classes have gradually gained ground in economic and public affairs. They began by claiming their rights in the socio-economic sphere. They extended their action then to claims on the political level. And, finally, they applied themselves to the acquisition of the benefits of a more refined culture. Today, therefore, workers all over the world bluntly refuse ever to be treated as if they were irrational objects without freedom, to be used at the arbitrary disposition of others. They insist that they be regarded as men with a share in every sector of human society; in the socio-economic sphere and in public life and in the fields of learning and culture."

9. John Paul II, "On Social Concerns, *Origins* (March 3, 1988), p. 654.

10. John Paul II, *Pilgrims of Peace* (Washington, D.C.: USCC, 1980), p. 46.

11. John Eagleson and Philip Scharper, *Puebla and Beyond* (Maryknoll, N.Y.: Orbis Books, 1979), p. 66.

Bibliography

Avila, Charles. *Ownership: Early Christian Teaching*. Maryknoll, N.Y.: Orbis Books, 1983.

Baile, Rachel. *Women and Jewish Law*. New York: Schocken Books, 1984.

Brandon, S. G. F. *Jesus and the Zealots*. Manchester: Manchester University Press, 1967.

Cassidy, Richard J. *Jesus, Politics and Society*. Maryknoll, N.Y.: Orbis Books, 1979.

Cook, Richard. "Jesus and the Pharisees: The Problem As It Stands Today," *Journal of Ecumenical Studies* 15 (1978), pp. 441–60.

Crossan, John D. *The Historical Jesus*. New York: HarperCollins, 1991.

Cullmann, Oscar. *Jesus and the Revolutionaries*. New York: Harper & Row, 1970.

Dudley, Donald. *Roman Society*. New York: Viking Penguin, 1970.

Eagleson, John and Philip Scharper, eds. *Puebla and Beyond*. Maryknoll, N.Y.: Orbis Books, 1979.

Echegaray, Hugo. *The Practice of Jesus*. Maryknoll, N.Y.: Orbis Books, 1980.

Fiorenza, Elisabeth Schüssler. *In Memory of Her*. New York: Crossroad, 1987.

Fisher, Eugene J., James A. Rudin, and Marc Tannenbaum. *Twenty Years of Jewish-Catholic Relations*. Mahwah, N.J.: Paulist Press, 1986.

Fisher, Eugene J. *Seminary Education and Christian-Jewish Relations*. Washington, D.C.: National Catholic Education Association, 1983.

Fitzmyer, Joseph A., S.J., *A Christological Catechism*. Mahwah, N.J.: Paulist Press, 1982.

Freyne, Sean. *The World of the New Testament.* Wilmington, Del.: Michael Glazier, 1980.

Flannery, Edward H. *The Anguish of the Jews.* Mahwah, N.J.: Paulist Press, 1985.

Josephus, Flavius. *Complete Works,* trans. William Whiston. Grand Rapids, Mich.: Kregel, 1981.

Gallup, George, Jr. and Jim Castelli. *The American Catholic People.* New York: Doubleday, 1987.

Grant, Michael, *The Army of the Caesars.* New York: Scribner's, 1974.
————. *The World of Rome.* New York: New American Library, 1987.

Gremillion, Joseph. *The Gospel of Peace and Justice.* Maryknoll, N.Y.: Orbis Books, 1976.

Harrington, Wilfred, O.P. *Mark.* Wilmington, Del.: Michael Glazier, 1985.

Hollyday, Joyce. "Voices Out of the Silence," *Sojourners* (June 1986), pp. 20–23.

Jeremias, Joachim. *The Parables of Jesus.* New York: Scribner's, 1972.
————. *Jerusalem in the Time of Jesus.* Philadelphia: Fortress Press, 1975.

John Paul II. "On Social Concerns," *Origins* (March 3, 1988), p. 654.
————. *Pilgrims of Peace.* Washington, D.C.: USCC, 1980.

Küng, Hans. *On Being A Christian.* New York: Doubleday, 1976.

Mattingly, Harold. *Christianity in the Roman Empire.* New York: W. W. Norton, 1967.

McKenzie, John L., S.J. *Dictionary of the Bible.* Milwaukee: Bruce Publishing, 1965.

Meier, John P. *A Marginal Jew.* New York: Doubleday, 1991.

Moloney, Francis J., S.D.B. *Women First Among the Faithful.* Notre Dame, Ind.: Ave Maria Press, 1986.

Moltmann-Wendel, Elisabeth. *The Women Around Jesus.* New York: Crossroad, 1987.

Musto, Ronald G. *The Catholic Peace Tradition.* Maryknoll, N.Y.: Orbis Books, 1986.

Neusner, Jacob. *From Politics to Piety.* Englewood Cliffs, N.J.: Prentice Hall, 1973.

New American Bible, Revised New Testament. National Conference of Catholic Bishops/United States Catholic Conference, 1986.

Nolan, Albert. *Jesus Before Christianity.* Maryknoll, N.Y.: Orbis Books, 1985.

O'Collins, Gerald, S.J. *What Are They Saying About Jesus?* Mahwah, N.J.: Paulist Press, 1977.

Pawlikowski, John T., O.S.M. *Christ in the Light of the Christian-Jewish Dialogue.* Mahwah, N.J.: Paulist Press, 1982.

————. *What Are They Saying About Christian-Jewish Relations?* Mahwah, N.J.: Paulist Press, 1980.

————. "Jesus and the Revolutionaries," *The Christian Century,* (Dec. 2, 1972), pp. 1237–41.

Perkins, Pheme. *Hearing the Parables of Jesus.* Mahwah, N.J.: Paulist Press, 1981.

Rivkin, Ellis. *What Crucified Jesus?* Nashville: Abingdon Press, 1984.

Ruether, Rosemary Radford. *Sexism and God-Talk.* Boston: Beacon Press, 1983.

Sloyan, Gerard S. *The Gospel of St. Mark.* Collegeville, Minn.: Liturgical Press, 1960.

Stagg, Evelyn and Frank. *Women in the World of Jesus.* Philadelphia: Westminster Press, 1978.

Steidl-Meier, Paul, S.J. *Social Justice Ministry.* New York: LeJacq, 1984.

Swift, Louis J. *The Early Fathers on War and Military Service.* Wilmington, Del.: William Glazier, 1983.

Thompson, William M. *The Jesus Debate.* Mahwah, N.J.: Paulist Press, 1985.

Wahlberg, Rachel Conrad. *Jesus According to a Woman.* Mahwah, N.J.: Paulist Press, 1986.

Watson, G. R. *The Roman Soldier.* Ithaca, N.Y.: Cornell University Press, 1969.

Wilken, Robert L. *The Christians as the Romans Saw Them.* New Haven, Conn.: Yale University Press, 1984.

Yoder, John Howard. *The Politics of Jesus.* Grand Rapids, Mich.: Eerdmans, 1972.

Index of
Scripture References

GERMANIA

GAUL

ITALIA

•Rome

HISPANIA

AFRICA

THE ROMAN EMPIRE
AT THE
TIME OF JESUS

SCALE IN MILES

0   300   600